Intermediate Repertoire 3

by James and Jane Smisor Bastien

KJOS Neil A. Kjos Music Company · *Publisher*

PREFACE

The INTERMEDIATE PIANO COURSE is designed to be used after the student has completed Level 4 of the BASTIEN PIANO LIBRARY. In addition, the INTERMEDIATE PIANO COURSE may be used by a student who has completed *any* elementary piano course. This course is a comprehensive, organized program of study consisting of four books per level which may be used simultaneously for best results. The INTERMEDIATE PIANO COURSE is available in grade levels 1, 2, 3, in each of the following books.

- INTERMEDIATE REPERTOIRE
- INTERMEDIATE THEORY
- INTERMEDIATE TECHNIC
- INTERMEDIATE MULTI-KEY SOLOS

INTERMEDIATE REPERTOIRE introduces the student to many factors of each style period: Baroque, Classical, Romantic, and Contemporary. For each period there are descriptions of overall styles (dress, art, architecture), keyboard instruments, various compositions representative of each period, and a list of composers. The music is a combination of master composer works and pieces written by the Bastiens in each style period. Special emphasis is given to providing more accessible pieces in the Romantic style. The teacher may assign pieces from different periods of the Repertoire book at the same time.

INTERMEDIATE THEORY contains written and playing material to coordinate with the Repertoire book.

INTERMEDIATE TECHNIC contains exercises and etudes by the standard composers as well as many new studies by the Bastiens.

INTERMEDIATE MULTI-KEY SOLOS provides a variety of original music by the Bastiens to encourage the student to explore many keys rather than staying in the limited key selection found in master composer works at the intermediate level.

The INTERMEDIATE PIANO COURSE includes the following books:

Intermediate Repertoire 1 (WP105)
Intermediate Repertoire 2 (WP106)
Intermediate Repertoire 3 (WP107)

Intermediate Theory 1 (WP108)
Intermediate Theory 2 (WP109)
Intermediate Theory 3 (WP110)

Intermediate Technic 1 (WP111)
Intermediate Technic 2 (WP112)
Intermediate Technic 3 (WP113)

Intermediate Multi-key Solos 1 (WP114)
Intermediate Multi-key Solos 2 (WP115)
Intermediate Multi-key Solos 3 (WP116)

Printed in USA.
ISBN #0-8497-5188-8

CONTENTS

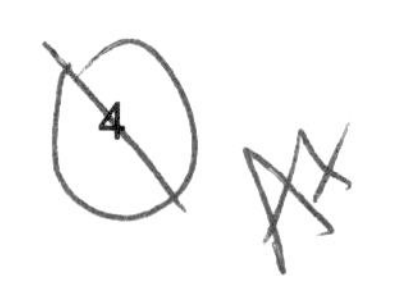

Allegro in A Minor

STYLE: ROMANTIC

JAMES BASTIEN

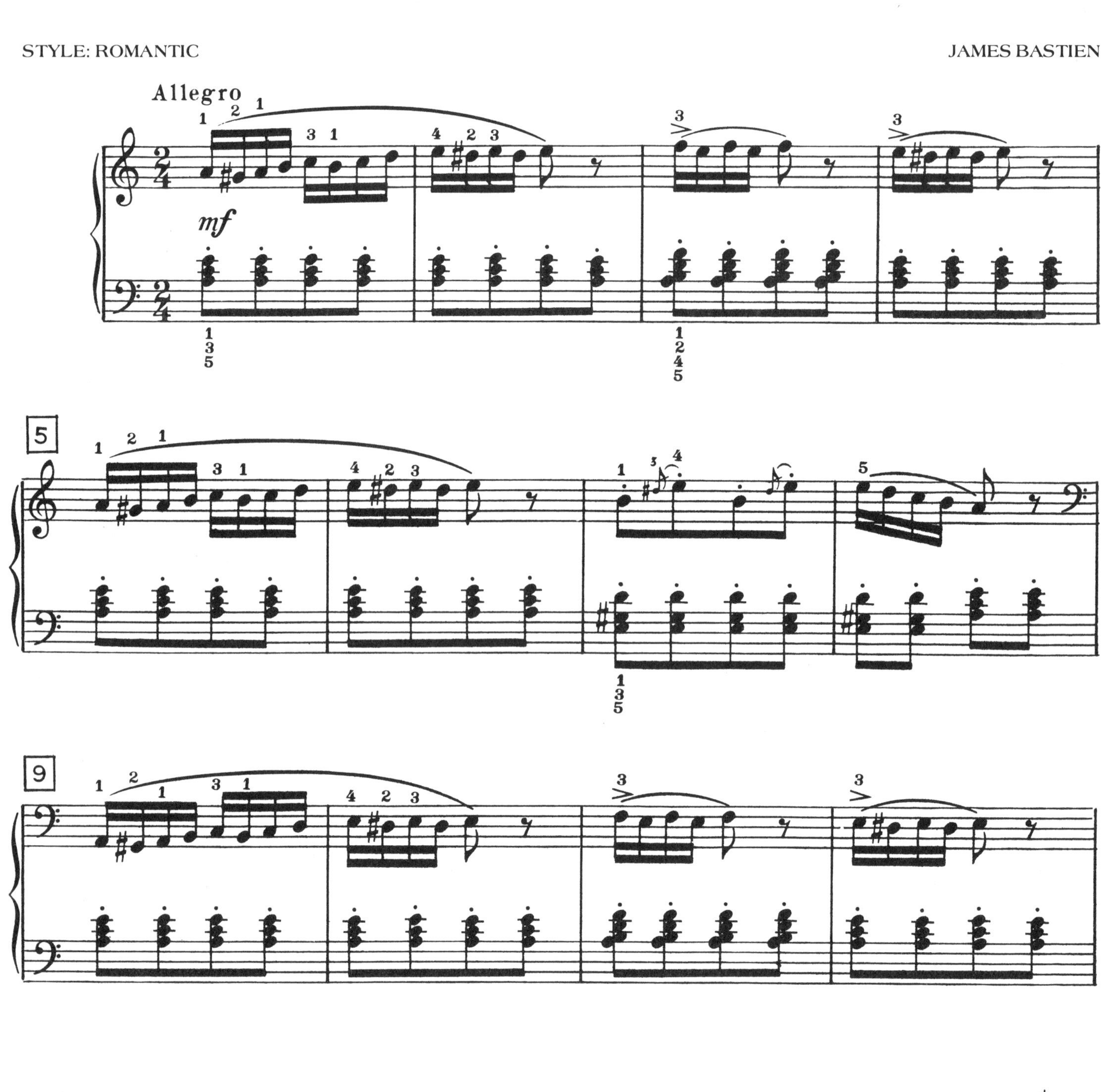

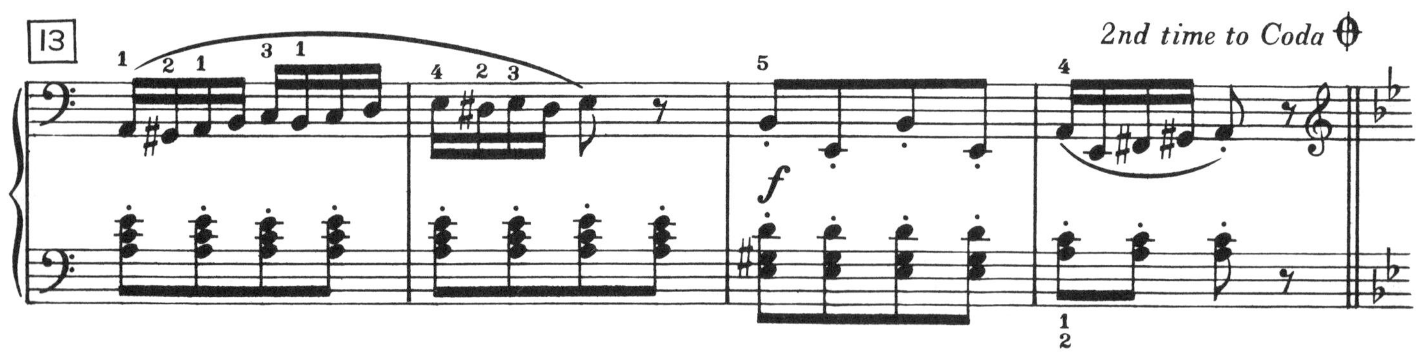

17
p
espressivo
22
27
D. C. al Coda
rit.
Coda
p
cresc.
mf
ff
8va

Ornaments

Ornaments are music signs printed above notes indicating melodic decoration. The two most commonly used baroque ornaments are the trill and the mordent.

Trill

The trill generally starts on the note above the printed note (either a half- or whole-step above the printed note). The trill has no set speed or length; it may be short or long, and may be played fast or slow.

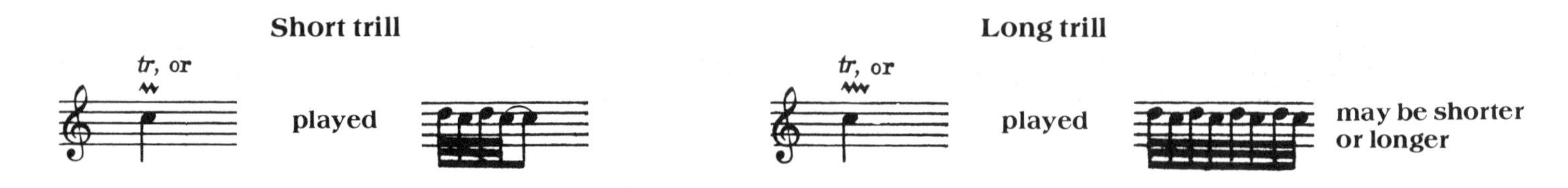

Practice these trills in preparation for music literature.*

Mordent

The mordent starts on the printed note with a quick alteration to the note a half- or whole-step below. The standard mordent has just three notes.

Practice these mordents in preparation for music literature.*

*The choice of fingering may be determined by student or teacher preference.

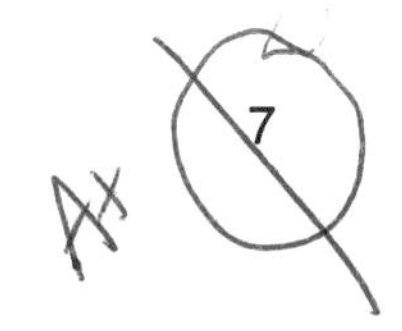

Minuet in F

STYLE: BAROQUE

JAMES BASTIEN

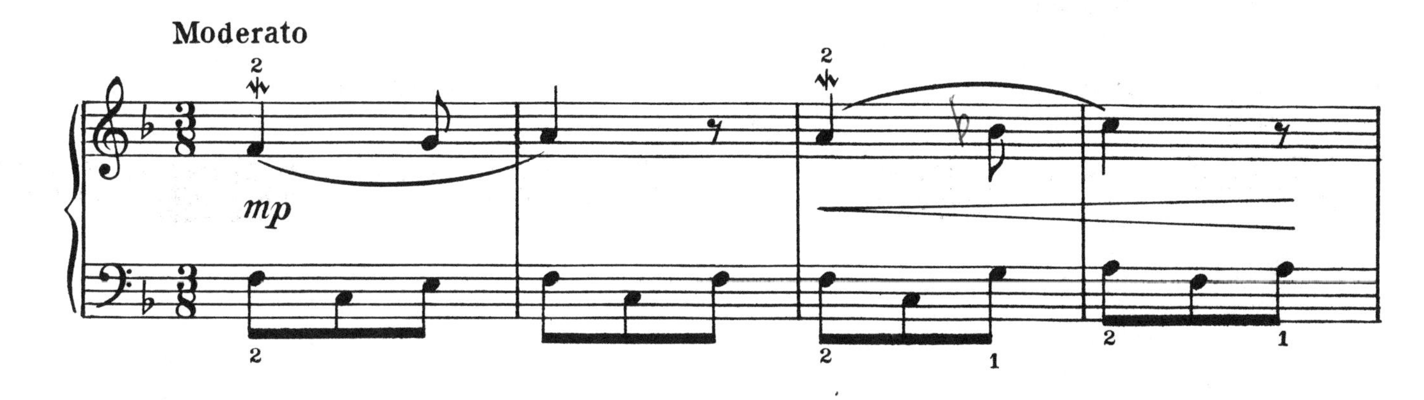

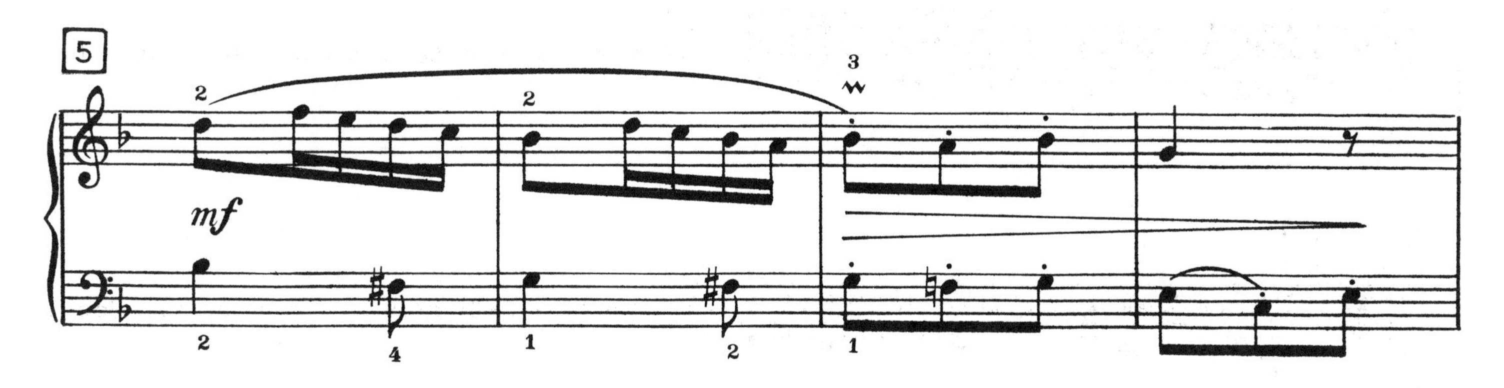

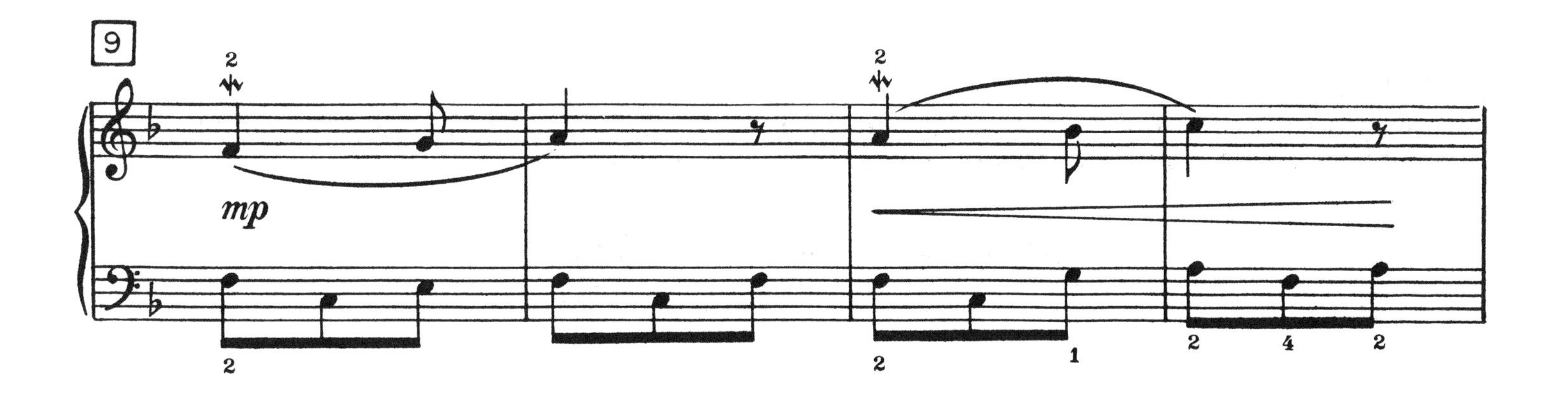

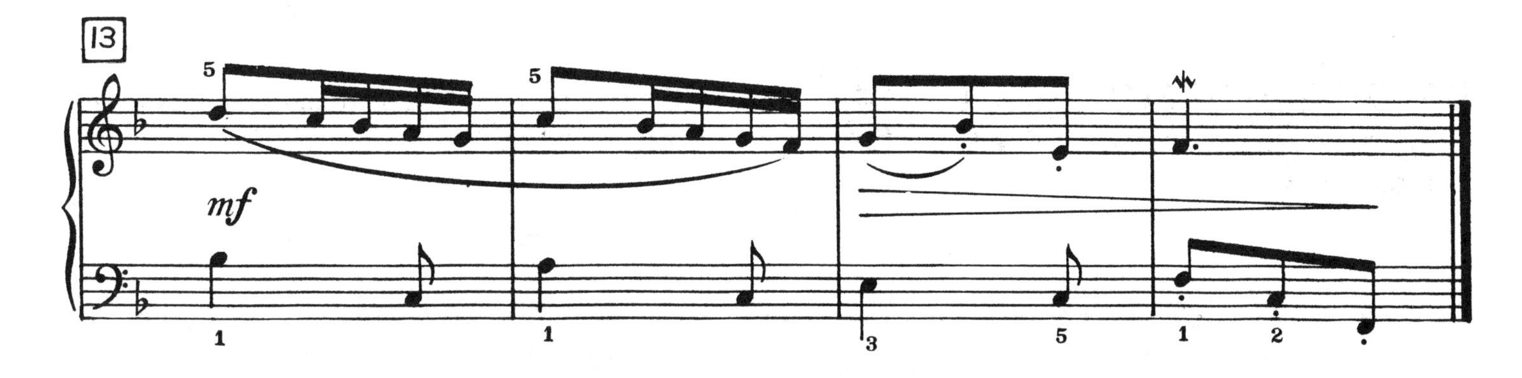

THE BAROQUE PERIOD

"Assumption of St. Mary"
by Peter Paul Rubens (1577-1640)

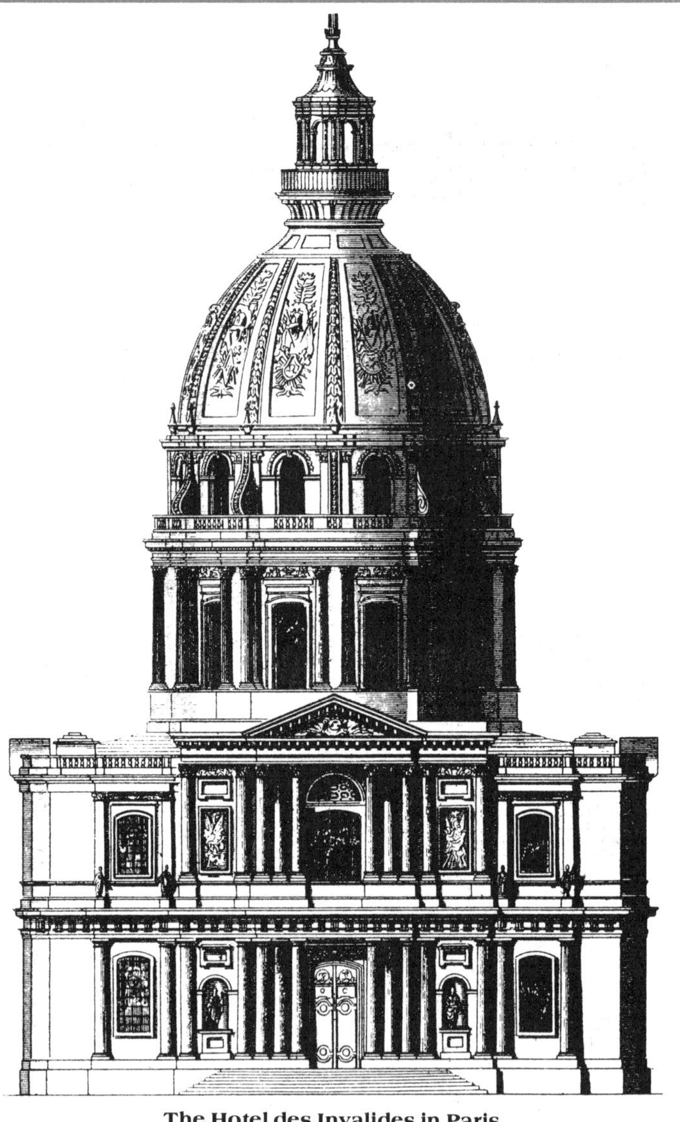

The Hotel des Invalides in Paris

Baroque Style

The Baroque period was a time in history (1600-1750) which had certain styles, customs, and characteristics. During this time people wore fancy clothes with lots of ruffles and decorations, and they also wore powdered wigs with many waves and curls. The art and architecture of this period also incorporated many ornamental decorations. Churches, palaces, and other buildings often were built on a large scale design and included much detail work.

Baroque Keyboard Music

The keyboard music in the Baroque period was frequently written in *two parts,* sometimes called *voices* (single notes in each hand).

from Passepied by Handel

A melody often consists of a short pattern (called a *motive*) which is repeated throughout a piece. One or more motives may be used in the composition.

from Air in D minor by Purcell

1600-1750

Baroque Forms

Much of the music was written as dance pieces such as the *minuet, march, gavotte, gigue,* and many others. Each dance has its own rhythm and style.

Baroque music often was written in *binary,* or two-part form. The two parts are called section A and section B, and usually each section is repeated: ‖: A :‖: B :‖

Baroque Keyboard Instruments

Before the invention of the piano, keyboard music was written for the *clavichord* and the *harpsichord.* The clavichord produces a small delicate sound and was used mainly in small rooms where it could be heard. The harpsichord has a bigger sound and was the favored instrument during the Baroque period. It is still popular today.

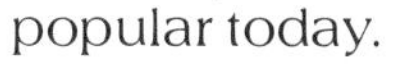

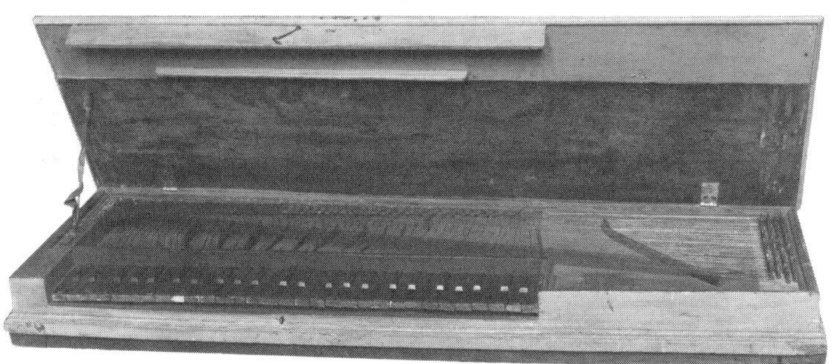

18th Century German Clavichord
From the Metropolitan Museum of Art, The Crosby Brown Collection of Musical Instruments, 1889.

18th Century French Harpsichord
From the Metropolitan Museum of Art, Gift of Susan Dwight Bliss, 1944.

Baroque Composers

The two best known Baroque composers are Johann Sebastian Bach (1685-1750) and George Frideric Handel (1685-1759), both Germans. The best known English composer from the Baroque period is Henry Purcell (1659-1695). Antonio Vivaldi (1678-1741) and Domenico Scarlatti (1685-1757) are two of the most famous Baroque Italian composers. Well known French Baroque composers include Jean Baptiste Lully (1632-1687), Françoise Couperin (1668-1733), and Jean-Philippe Rameau (1683-1764).

Bach, Scarlatti, Rameau, and Couperin wrote a great deal of music for the harpsichord. Their keyboard music is played frequently in concerts today on either a piano or a harpsichord.

Johann Sebastian Bach (1685-1750), a German composer, had numerous relatives who were musicians: from seven generations, 193 out of 200 were musicians. Bach's parents died when he was 10 years old, and his oldest brother, Johann Christopher, raised him. His brother died when Johann Sebastian was 15. Following that, Johann Sebastian lived at the St. Michael School where he studied music and was a choirboy. At 19, Bach obtained a position as organist at a church in Arnstadt. Throughout his life he held positions at various churches and in royal courts, and for almost 30 years he was director of music at the St. Michael School in Leipzig. He was married twice and had 20 children, several of whom became well-known musicians. On his second wife's 25th birthday, he gave her (Anna Magdalena) a notebook containing pieces for members of his family to play. His best known easier clavier pieces come from this notebook. Bach was a prolific composer; his complete works fill 46 large volumes containing choral music, concertos, orchestral and chamber works, and organ and clavier music.

The musette is a French bagpipe which was popular in the 17th and 18th centuries. The title musette is given to dance pieces using the drone bass sound (repetition of the same note) suggestive of the bagpipe.

Musette in D Major

from "Notebook for Anna Magdalena Bach"

STYLE: BAROQUE

J.S. BACH

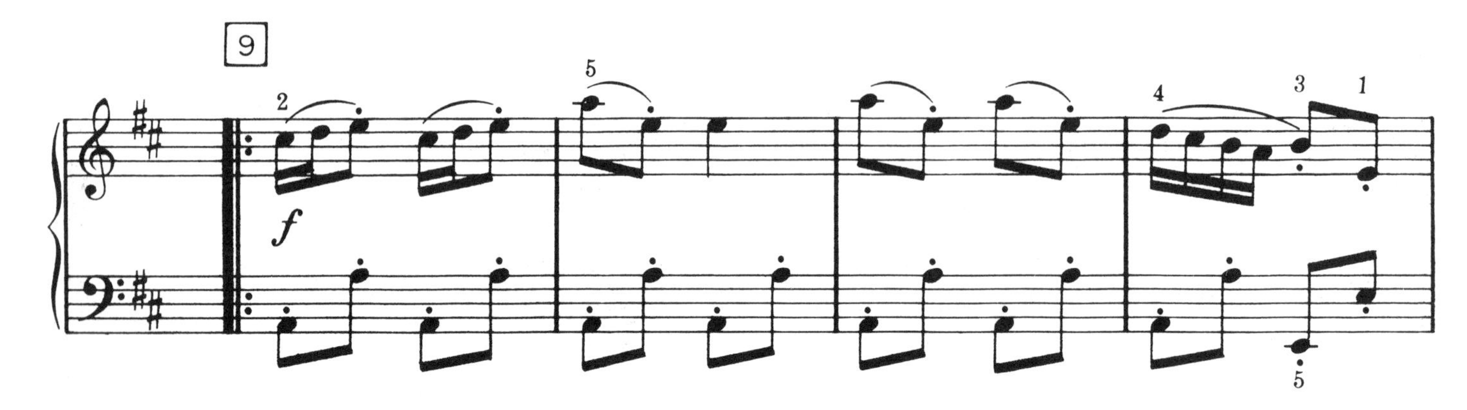

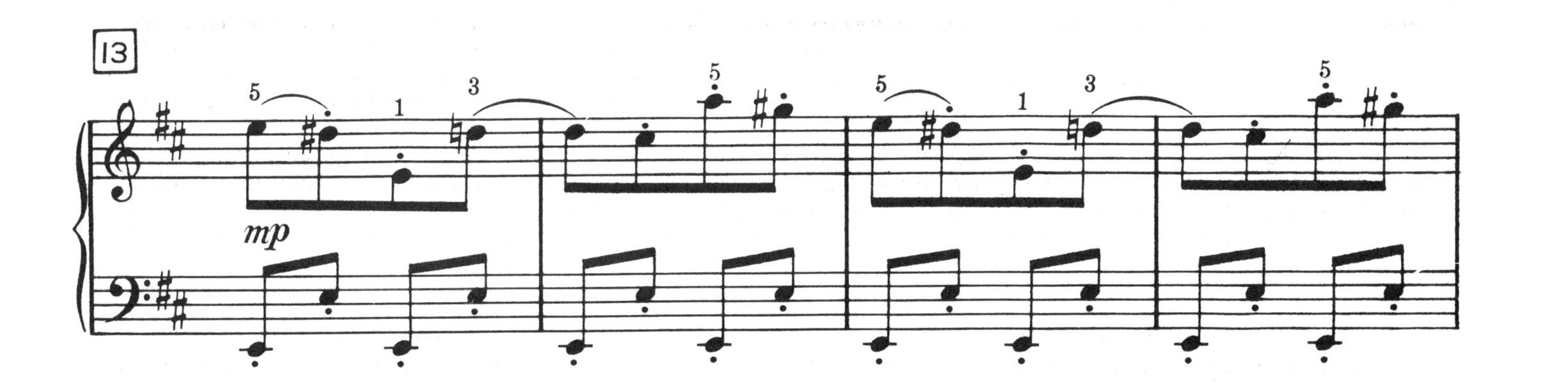
13
mp

17
cresc.

21
f

25

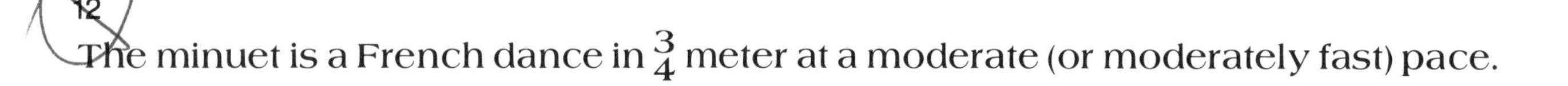

The minuet is a French dance in $\frac{3}{4}$ meter at a moderate (or moderately fast) pace.

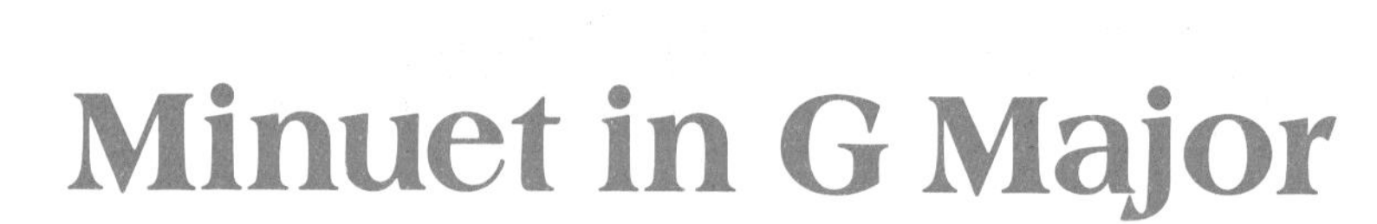

Minuet in G Major

from "Notebook for Anna Magdalena"

STYLE: BAROQUE

J.S. BACH

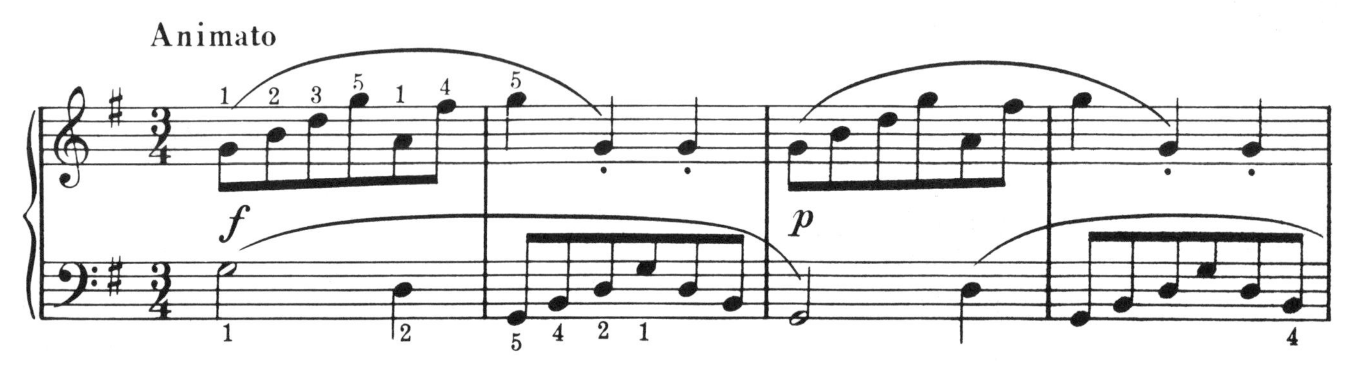

17
p
f
22
p
27
cresc.
32
f
p
36
f

The prelude is a short piece usually based on a single theme.

Prelude in C Major

from "Twelve Short Preludes"

STYLE: BAROQUE

J.S. BACH

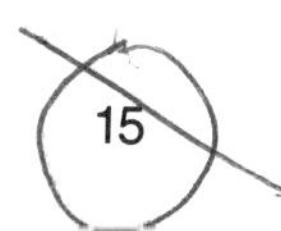

Henry Purcell (1659-1695) was the greatest English composer of the Baroque era. He held various posts as singer, organist, and composer. He wrote an opera *Dido and Aeneas,* music for plays, songs, instrumental music, and some harpsichord music. His music reflects vocal qualities of lyricism and great expressiveness.

The air (or aria) is a song of lyrical character found in operas and other vocal works.

Air

STYLE: BAROQUE

HENRY PURCELL

Domenico Scarlatti (1685-1757) was the son of the composer Alessandro Scarlatti. Although born and raised in Naples, Italy, Domenico spent most of his career in Madrid, Spain, under the patronage of Queen Maria Barbara. He wrote more than 500 short pieces for the harpsichord. Although he titled most of these works sonatas, they are similar to brief etudes which use one particular technical device or figuration. His keyboard music is colorful and original and is played frequently in concert by harpsichordists and pianists.

Practice ornaments alone before adding them to this piece.

Minuet in C

STYLE: ROMANTIC

DOMENICO SCARLATTI

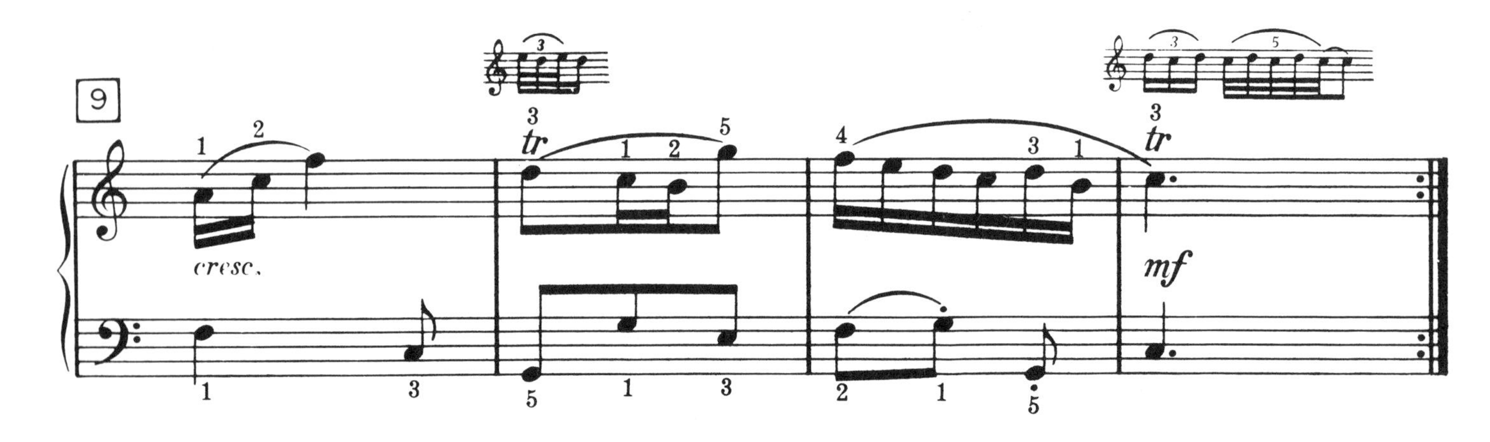

13
mf
p
17
mf
tr
p
21
25
cresc.
tr
mf

Arpeggios

An arpeggio is a broken (spread-out) chord.

Practice these arpeggio exercises. Repeat each several times. Turn the thumb under quickly, or cross over the thumb quickly. Play slowly at first, then increase the tempo.

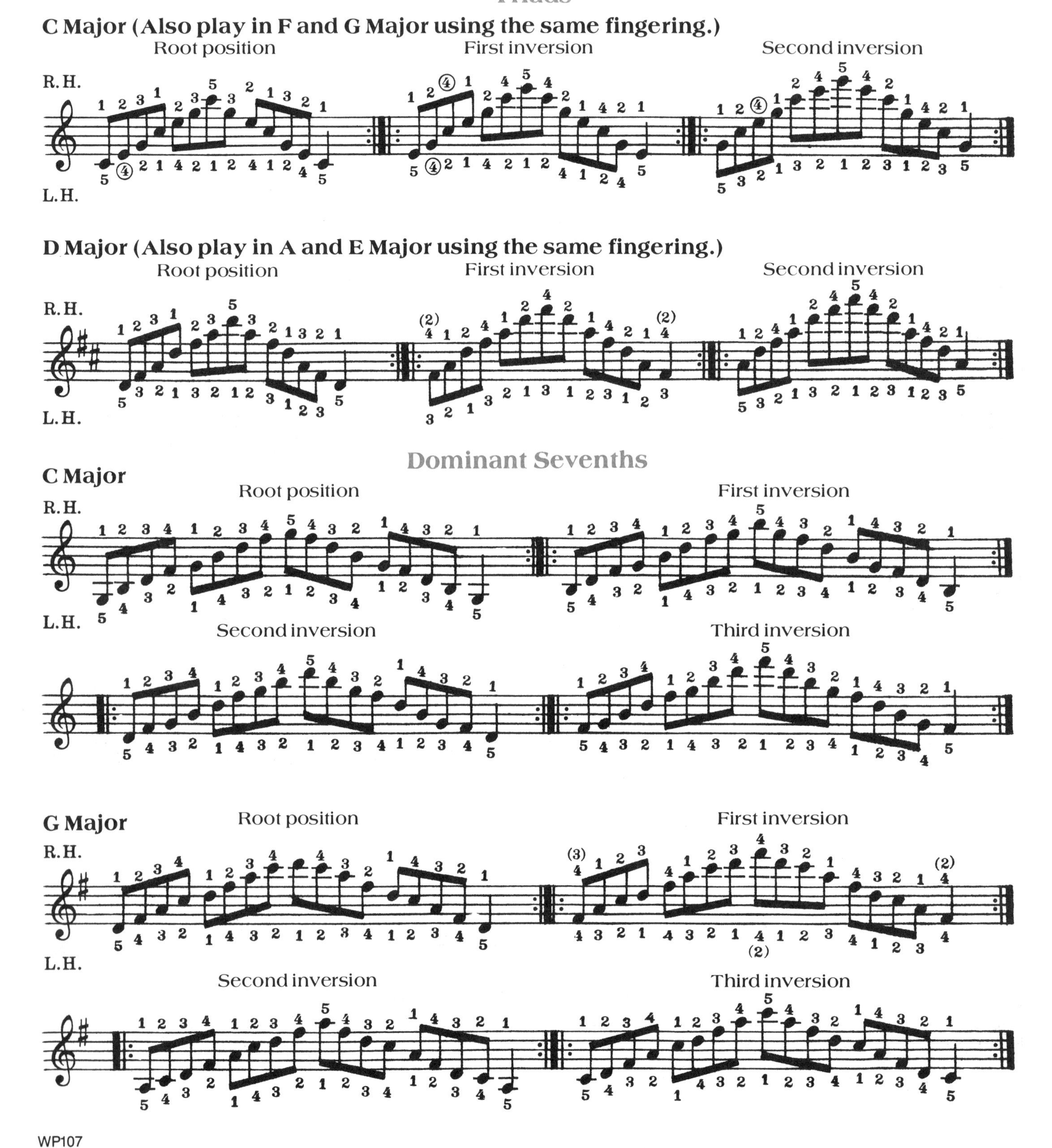

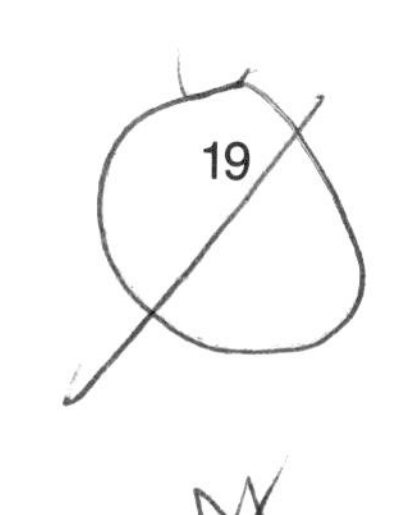

Etude in G

STYLE: CLASSICAL

JANE SMISOR BASTIEN

THE CLASSICAL PERIOD

"Death of Socrates"
by Jacques Louïs David (1750-1820). Courtesy of Metropolitan Museum of Art, Wolfe Fund, 1931.

The Pantheon in Paris

Classical Style

The Classical period, dating from about 1750-1820, was a time of change from the decorative Baroque to a more simple style. People wore clothes that were tailored in a less complicated manner than in the Baroque period, and people stopped wearing wigs with fancy stylings. The art and architecture of the period also reflected many of these changes. Buildings were built with simple, graceful, "classical" lines defined by balanced form.

Classical Keyboard Music

The keyboard music in the Classical period was frequently written in balanced phrase groupings lasting two, four, or eight measures.

from Minuet in C by Mozart

The style of writing often consists of a solo line with chordal accompaniment, rather than the two-voice style of the Baroque.

from Écossaise in G by Beethoven.

1750-1820

Classical Forms

Although dance pieces (minuet, etc.) were still written in the Classical period, expanded forms such as the *sonata allegro* and the *rondo* emerged.

In the first movements of sonatas and sonatinas ("little" sonatas), the form is usually *ternary*, or three-part form. The three parts are called *exposition* (A), *development* (B), and *recapitulation* (A): A B A.

The Early Piano

Credit is given to the Italian, Bartolomeo Cristofori, for producing the first piano in 1709. He was curator of musical instruments for the wealthy Medici family in Florence. At about the same time, other people had also invented the piano: Marius in France (1716) and Schröter in Germany (1717). Cristofori called his invention a *gravicembalo col piano e forte* (a keyboard instrument that can play soft and loud). The ability of the early piano to produce graded dynamics (crescendos and decrescendos), plus its light, silvery tone and sustaining quality was a tremendous change from the clavichord and harpsichord.

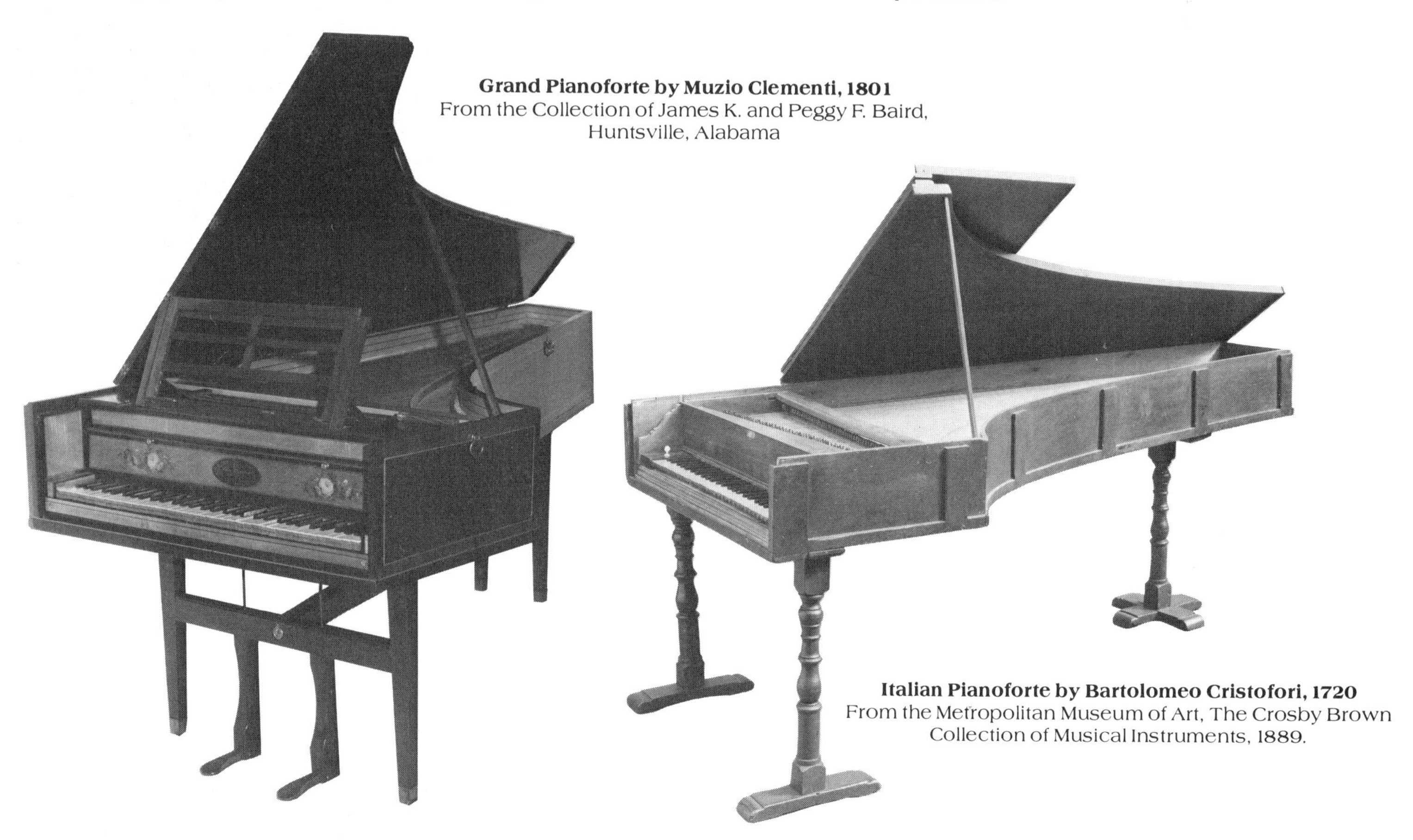

Grand Pianoforte by Muzio Clementi, 1801
From the Collection of James K. and Peggy F. Baird, Huntsville, Alabama

Italian Pianoforte by Bartolomeo Cristofori, 1720
From the Metropolitan Museum of Art, The Crosby Brown Collection of Musical Instruments, 1889.

Classical Composers

The three most famous classical composers are Franz Joseph Haydn (1732-1809), Wolfgang Amadeus Mozart (1756-1791), and Ludwig van Beethoven (1770-1827). All three composers either studied or lived in Vienna, Austria. The Italian, Muzio Clementi (1752-1832) is another composer from this period now best remembered for his keyboard sonatinas.

These four composers wrote a great deal of piano music which they performed themselves. Mozart, Beethoven, and Clementi were especially prominent as pianists.

Franz Joseph Haydn (1732-1809), an Austrian composer, studied singing, violin, and clavier as a youth and became a choirboy at the Vienna Cathedral. He spent more than 30 years in the service of Prince Esterhazy, a Hungarian nobleman, at Eisenstadt. Haydn was a major influence in the development of the symphony, sonata, and string quartet. During his long life he composed approximately 83 string quartets, more than 50 piano sonatas, 200 songs, over 100 symphonies, 18 operas, a vast amount of church music, concertos, and many other works.

Allegro Scherzando

STYLE: CLASSICAL

FRANZ JOSEPH HAYDN

22
p
26
mf
30
f
34
p
mf
f
39
p
f
ff

Muzio Clementi (1752-1832) was a famous Italian pianist, composer, and teacher. In 1781 he and Mozart had a contest to determine which one was the better pianist. Although no winner was announced, Clementi was thought to have a better technique, but the audience felt that Mozart was a finer musician. Clementi wrote *The Art of Playing on the Piano-Forte* which he used with his beginning students. Chopin also used this book with his students. In addition to his teaching, composing, and performing, Clementi established a successful piano factory and a publishing company.

Sonatina

Op. 36, No. 1

STYLE: CLASSICAL

MUZIO CLEMENTI

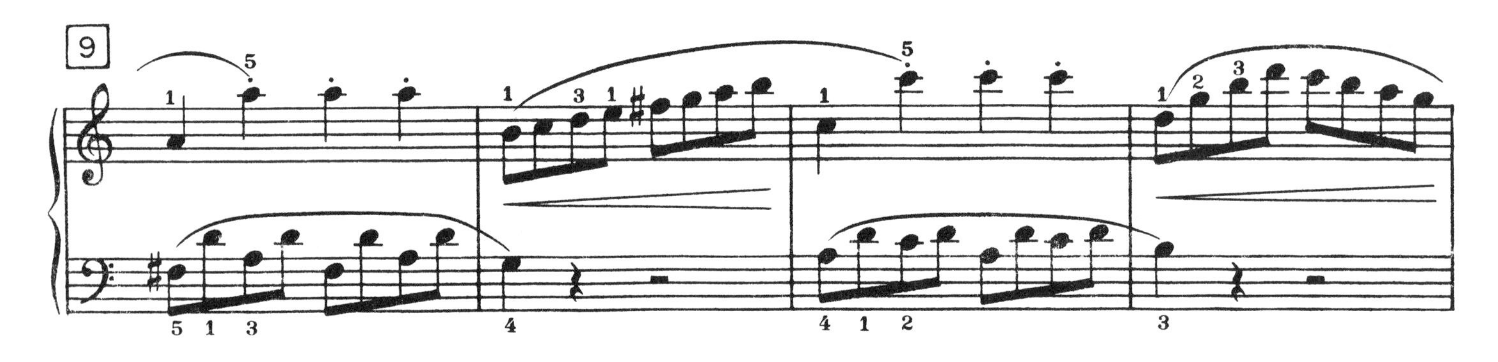

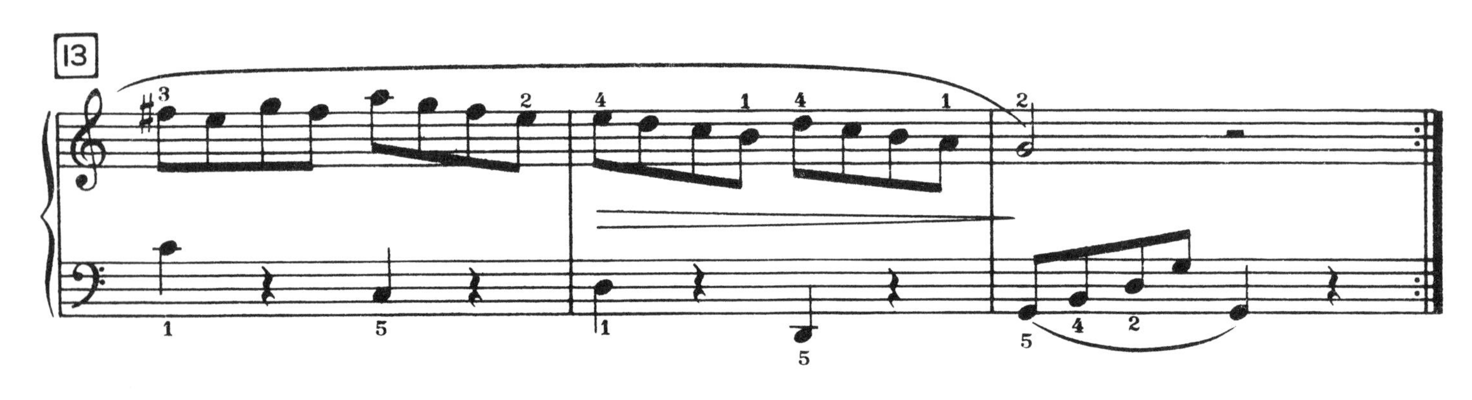

DEVELOPMENT
First Theme
16
p
f
21
RECAPITULATION
First Theme
p
26
cresc.
Second Theme
31
f
35

Andante
First Theme
mp dolce
tr
4
7
fz
p
10
f

Second Theme
13
fz
p
fz
p

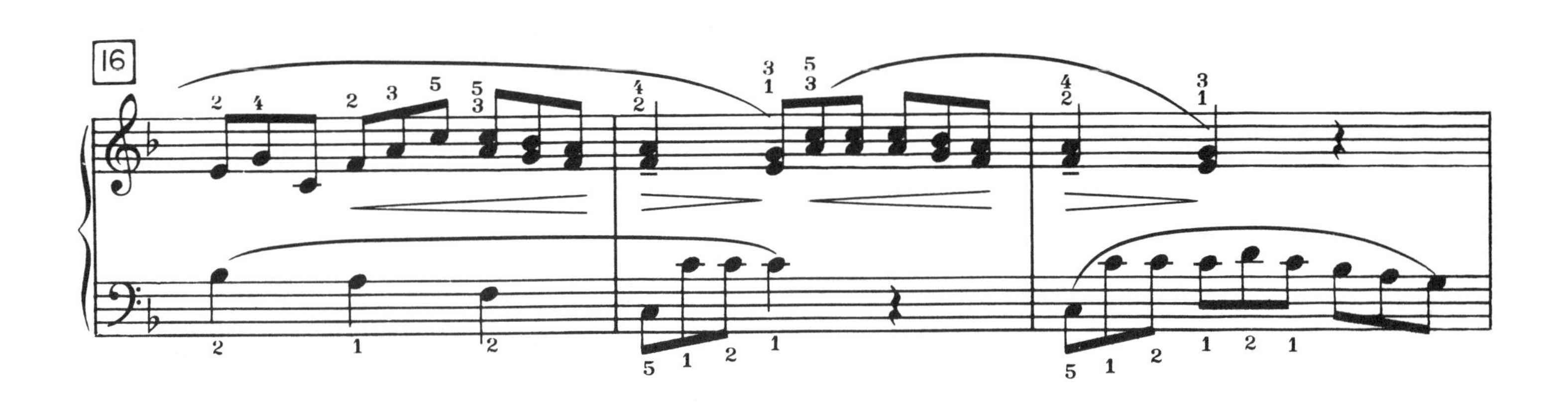
16

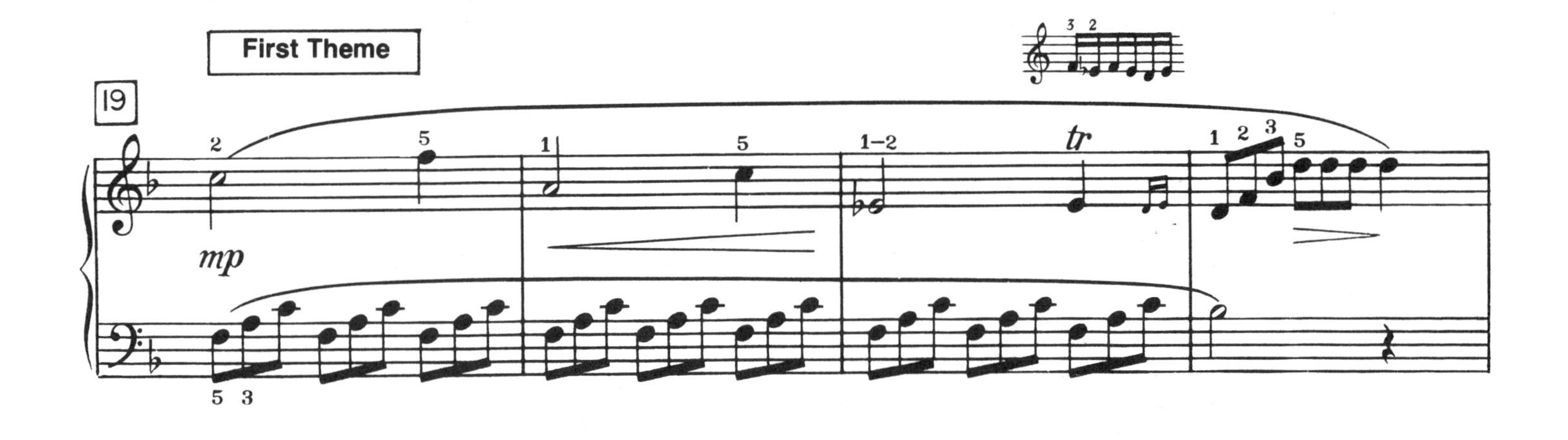
First Theme
19
mp
tr

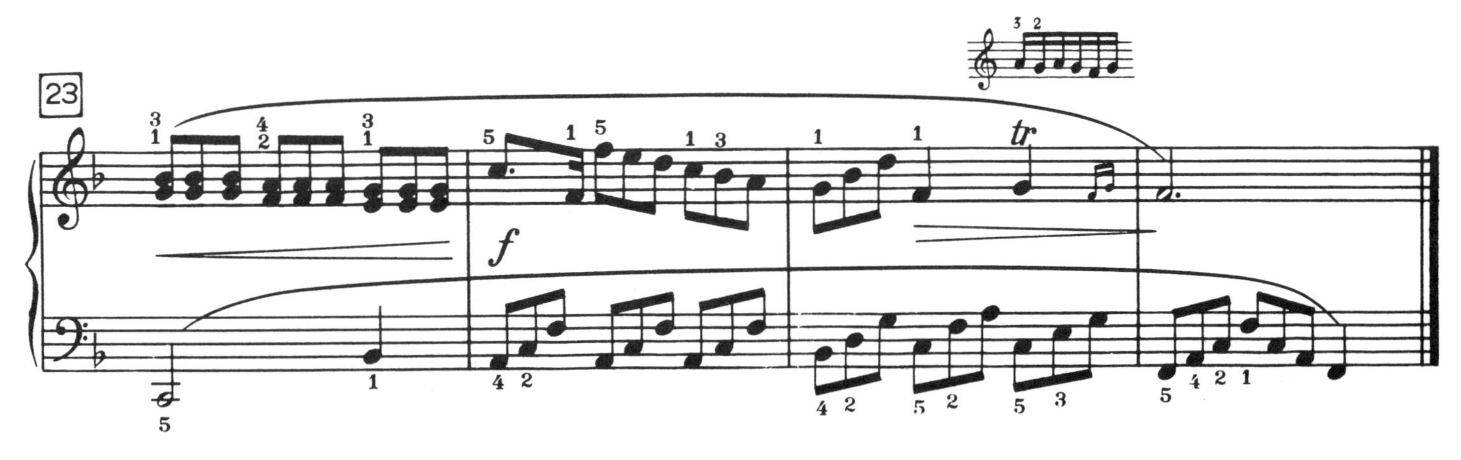
23
f
tr

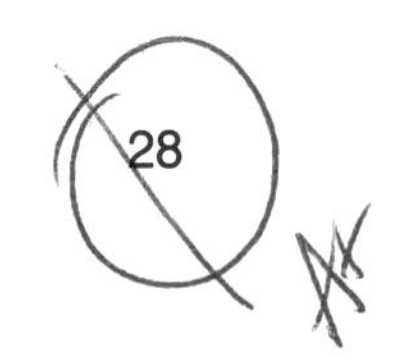

Vivace
First Theme
mf
legato
7
f
14
Transition
p
20
p
f
Second Theme
26

First Theme
dim.
mf
legato
f
Second Theme
p
p
cresc.
ff

Ludwig van Beethoven (1770-1827), a German composer, grew up in Bonn where he studied violin and piano. Later, he studied briefly in Vienna with Haydn for about a year. Beethoven earned his living from the sale of compositions and from teaching. In his early thirties, he experienced a hearing loss which later deteriorated into total deafness. He grew morose and suspicious and had frequent outbursts of temper. A prolific composer, Beethoven wrote 32 piano sonatas, five piano concertos, one violin concerto, an opera, a great deal of chamber music, and many other works.

Für Elise

STYLE: CLASSICAL

LUDWIG VAN BEETHOVEN

24
p cantando
legato
28
cresc.
dim
32
p
p
35
p
dim.
39
a tempo
e poco rit. pp

44
mf
49
dim.
54
pp
START
60
p
cresc.
f
66
dim
p
cresc.
72
f
dim.
G#

78
pp
A
cresc.
82
dim.
rall.
a tempo
pp
86
91
mf
dim.
96
pp
101
dim. e rit.

THE ROMANTIC PERIOD

"Stoke-by-Nayland"
by John Constable (1836). Courtesy of
The Art Institute of Chicago.

The Papal Cancellaria in Rome

Romantic Style

The Romantic period dating from about 1820-1900 was a time of personal expression. The impact of the French Revolution (1789-1794) set the stage for freedom and free-thinking individuals who set out in different artistic directions. Even in dress expressive beauty was portrayed. Women wore hoop skirts and decorative clothing with lace and/or embroidery. Men wore ruffled shirts, wide bow ties, and elegant clothes. Strong emphasis on emotion and imagination is found in literature, art, and architecture.

Romantic Keyboard Music

The music of the Romantic period often contains warm, beautiful melodies (so tuneful that many have been made into popular songs).

The accompaniment often colors and supports the melody.

Frequently, expressive indications such as *espressivo* (expressively) and *dolce* (sweetly), etc. are used to aid the performer in interpreting the beautiful melodies. Color is added to the piano by more frequent use of pedal; pedal indications were used a great deal by Romantic composers.

1820-1900

Romantic Forms

During the Romantic period large works such as the sonata were still used, but intimate small works such as the waltz, rhapsody, impromptu, romance, ballade, nocturne, étude (study piece), and many others, were written with increasing frequency.

National folk music was used in works such as the polonaise and mazurka by the Polish composer, Chopin, and in the Hungarian rhapsody by Liszt, who was Hungarian.

The short works are often written in three-part song form: **A B A**.

The Piano in the Romantic Period

During the Romantic period the piano developed into a larger and more resonant instrument than the early piano in the Classical period. Development and perfection of the piano included a larger sound board, a heavier metal frame, thicker strings strung with more tension, a larger keyboard range, and a better pedal mechanism. All these factors aided in providing an instrument with a greater tone.

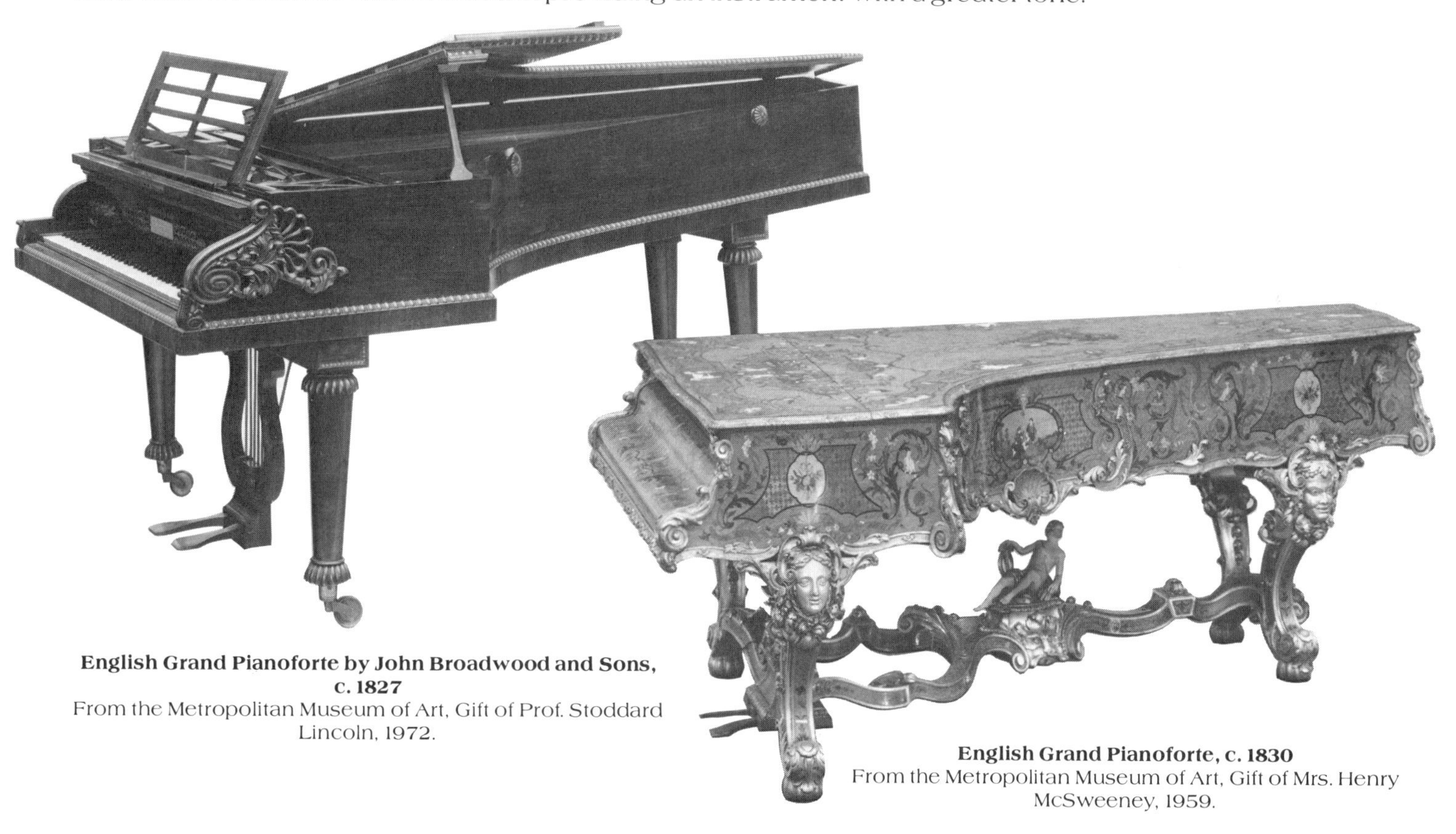

English Grand Pianoforte by John Broadwood and Sons, c. 1827
From the Metropolitan Museum of Art, Gift of Prof. Stoddard Lincoln, 1972.

English Grand Pianoforte, c. 1830
From the Metropolitan Museum of Art, Gift of Mrs. Henry McSweeney, 1959.

Romantic Composers

Ludwig van Beethoven (1770-1827) bridged the Classical and Romantic periods reflecting Classical influences in his early music and Romantic influences in his middle and later years. The most famous Romantic keyboard composers are Franz Schubert (1797-1828), Felix Mendelssohn (1809-1847), Frédéric Chopin (1810-1849), Robert Schumann (1810-1856), Franz Liszt (1811-1886), and Johannes Brahms (1833-1897). Other Romantic keyboard composers include César Franck (1822-1890), Modest Mussorgsky (1839-1881), Peter Ilyich Tchaikovsky (1840-1893), and Edvard Grieg (1843-1907).

The mazurka is a Polish national dance in $\frac{3}{4}$ meter, the basic rhythm being: $\frac{3}{4}$ ♪.♬ ♩ ♩. The main characteristics of the mazurka are the use of dotted rhythms and strong accents on the second and third beats, often at the ends of phrases. Chopin was the first prominent composer to devote so much of his creative effort to this nationalistic music; he wrote over 50 mazurkas in various styles and moods.

Mazurka

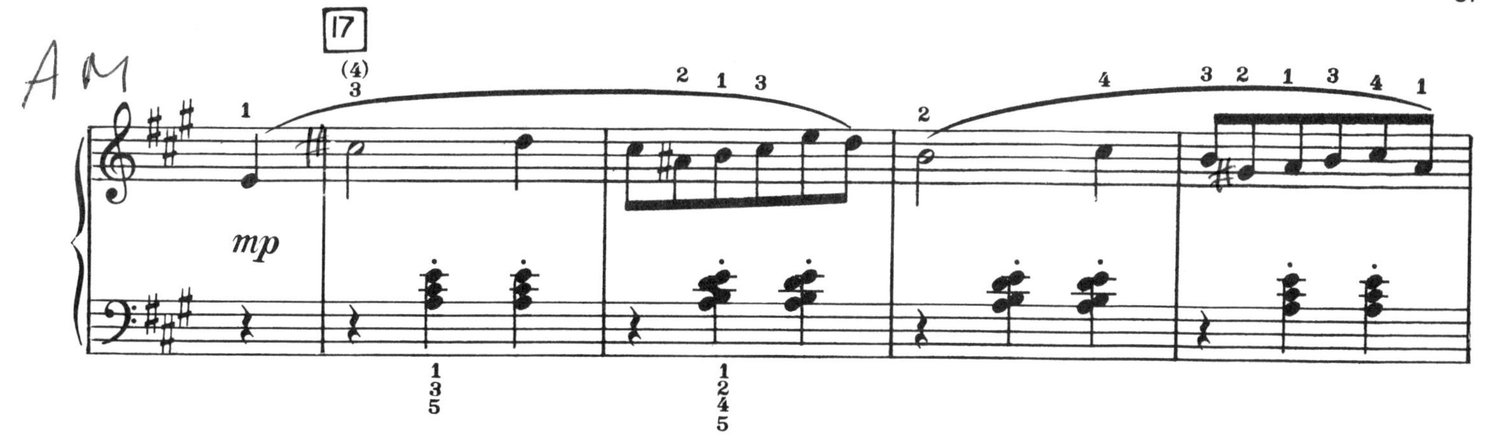
A M
17
mp

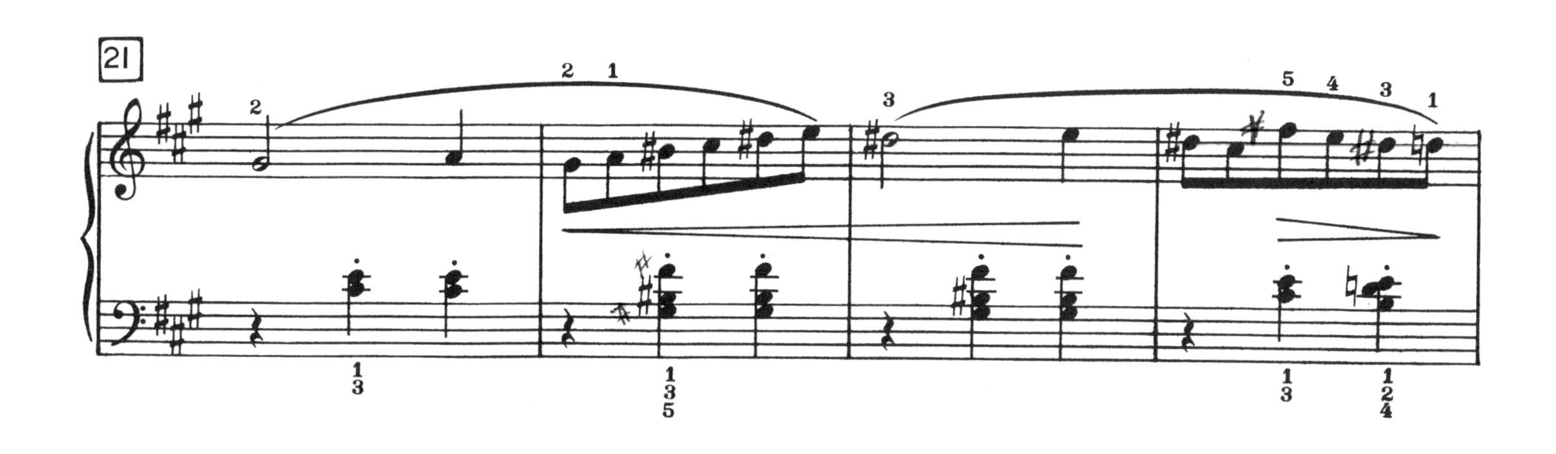
21

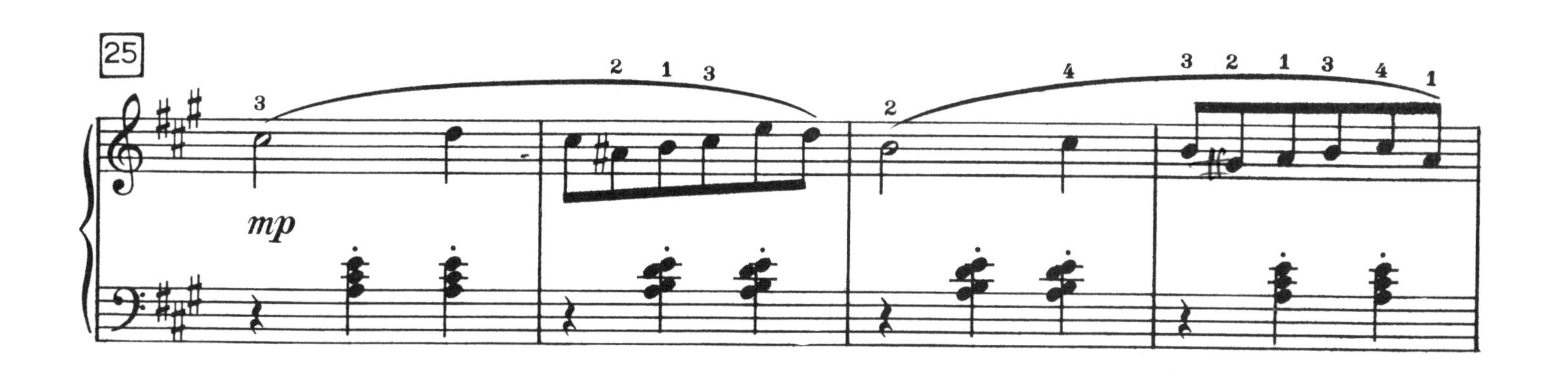
25
mp

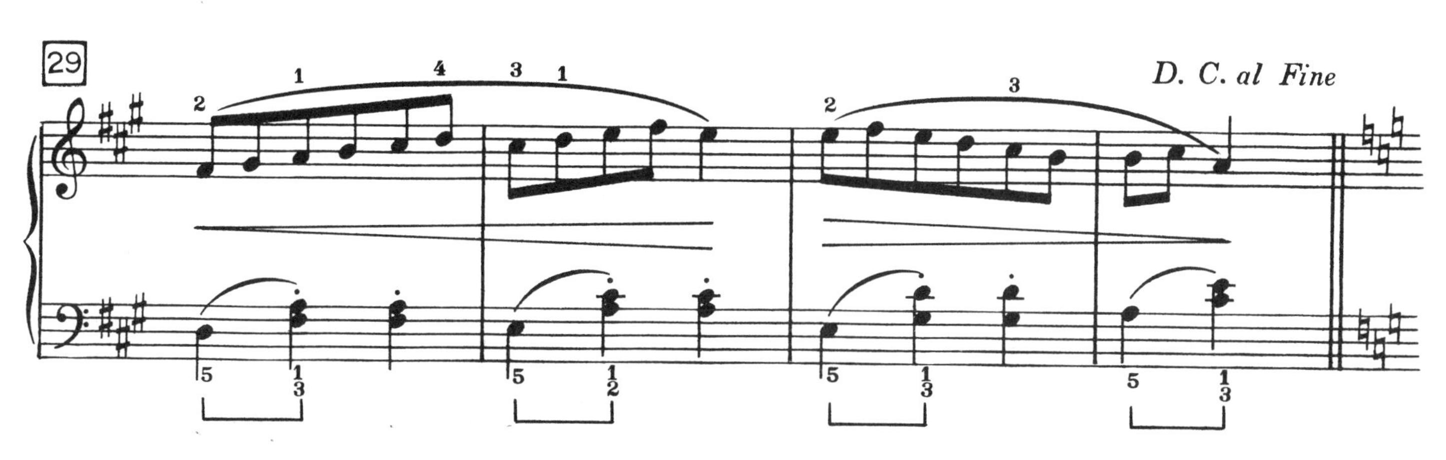
29
D. C. al Fine

The French word nocturne means night piece; it is a descriptive word used to depict the calm beauty of the night. The name was first used on piano pieces by John Field (1782-1837), an Irish pianist and composer. However, Chopin adopted it and wrote beautiful nocturnes with expressive melodies often accompanied by arpeggiated chordal figures.

Nocturne

STYLE: ROMANTIC

JAMES BASTIEN

13
cresc.
mf
16
a tempo
rit. molto
mp
19
p
mp
22
25
dim. e rit.
pp

Albert Elmenreich (1816-1905), a German composer, had a dual career as an actor and as a composer of several operas for which he wrote his own libretto. His popular *Spinning Song* for piano is a favorite all over the world.

Spinning Song

Op. 14

STYLE: ROMANTIC

ALBERT ELMENREICH
1816-1905

27
p
33
mp
39
mp
45
D. C. al Coda
Coda
dim. e rit.

Felix Mendelssohn (1809-1847), a German composer and pianist, was born in Hamburg of well-to-do parents. When Felix was three, his parents moved to Berlin where his schooling began with private tutors. He first performed in public at the age of nine; he began to compose at the age of 12. Mendelssohn wrote his famous overture to *A Midsummer Night's Dream* when he was 17. He traveled extensively through England, Scotland, and the continent. His trips inspired him to write the descriptive overture, *Fingal's Cave*, and his *Symphony No. 3* ("Scotch") while in Scotland. A visit to Italy resulted in the *Symphony No. 4* ("Italian"). In 1829 Mendelssohn conducted Bach's *St. Matthew Passion* which was the first performance of a major work by Bach since his death almost 80 years earlier. The result was a revival of interest in Bach's music. Mendelssohn's interest in choral music inspired him to compose the oratorios *St. Paul* (1836), and for presentation in England, *Elijah* (1846). Mendelssohn was an extremely busy musician acting as a pianist, conductor of orchestras in Dusseldorf and Leipzig, and founder and dean of the Leipzig Conservatory, where he taught piano and composition. His health was never robust, and these taxing musical activities plus a whirlwind social life strained his constitution severely. He literally wore himself out and died of apoplexy at the age of 38. He was a prolific composer: his works include orchestral music, the *Violin Concerto in E Minor* (1844), piano concertos, choral and vocal music, chamber music, organ works, and well-known piano works such as the *Andante and Rondo Capriccioso*, *Variations Sérieuses* and eight books of *Songs Without Words.*

Romanze

STYLE: ROMANTIC

FELIX MENDELSSOHN

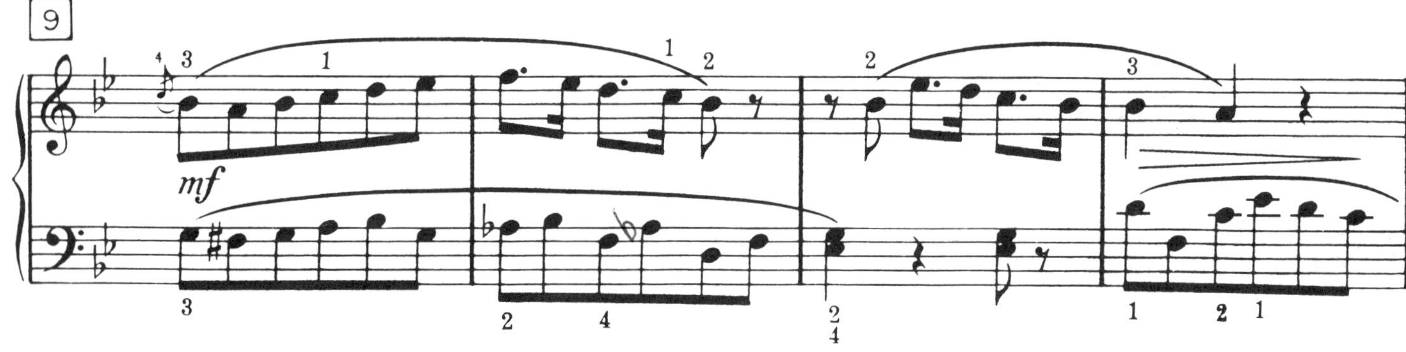

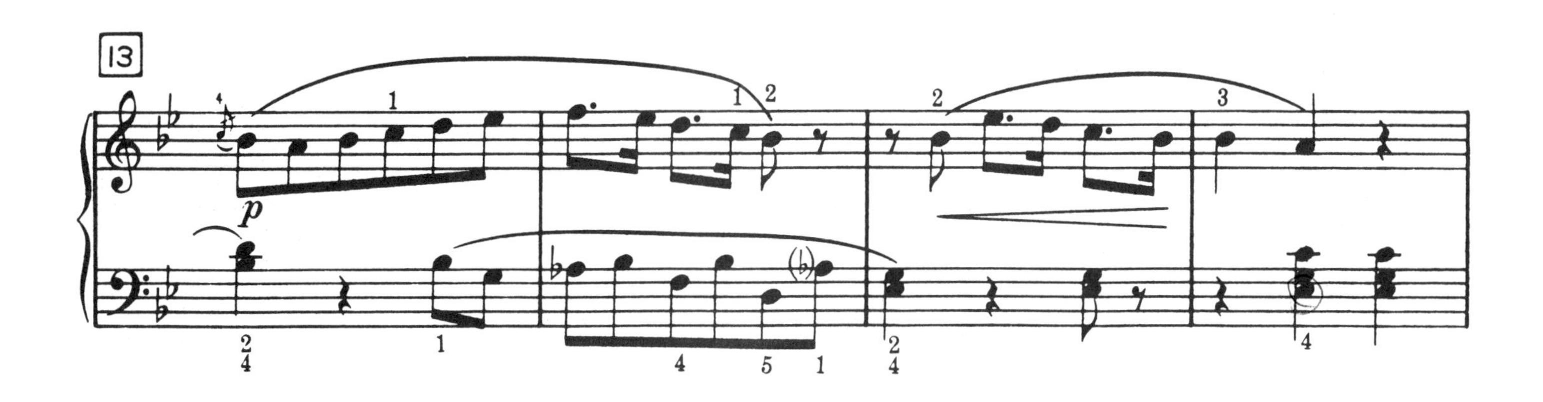
13
p

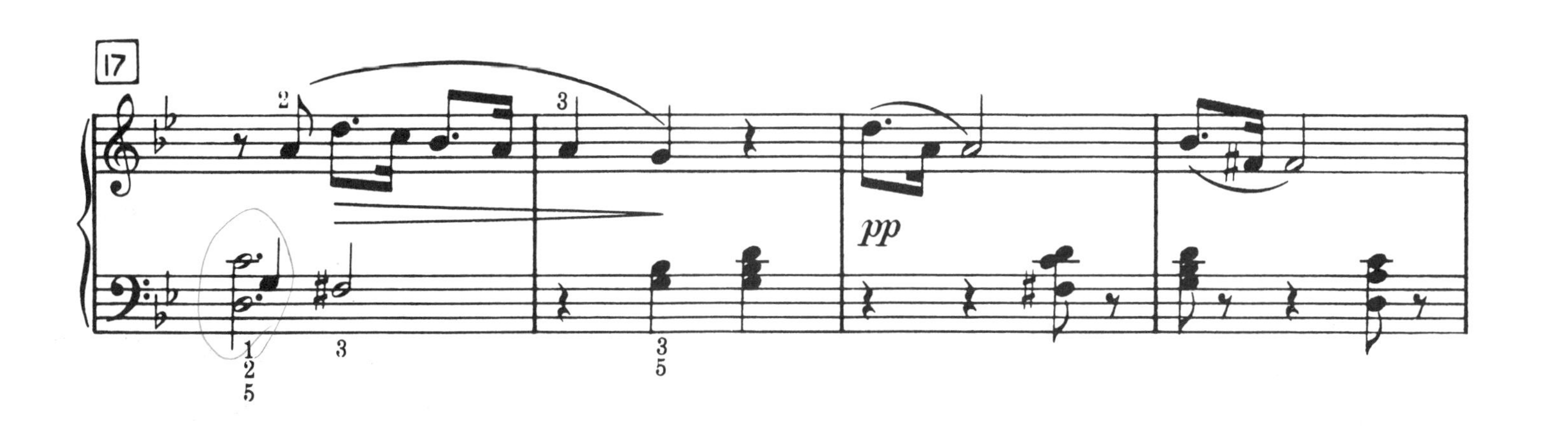
17
pp

21

25
rit. e dim.

Edvard Grieg (1843-1907), a Norwegian composer, received his first musical instruction from his mother, and he began composing at the age of nine. Grieg studied in Leipzig, Germany, at the Conservatory and graduated after four years of study. He was granted an annuity from the Norwegian government which enabled him to devote most of his time to composition. He spent his later years in his home (now a national museum) at Troldhougen near Bergen overlooking a beautiful fjord. His most popular works include many songs (*I Love Thee* being the best known), *Peer Gynt Suite No. 1, Lyric Pieces* (10 books for piano), and his popular *Piano Concerto in A Minor.*

Sailor's Song

Op. 68, No. 1

STYLE: ROMANTIC

EDVARD GRIEG

Allegro vivace e marcato

cresc. molto

24
a tempo
poco rit.
ff
poco a poco rit.
29
a tempo
p
mp
34
mf
39
cresc. molto
44
a tempo
poco rit.
ff
poco a poco rit.

Robert Schumann (1810-1856), a German composer, was a child prodigy who played the piano when he was six years old and composed his first piano pieces when he was seven. He studied in Leipzig with Friedrich Wieck, whose daughter he later married. Schumann was not able to continue his career as a pianist because of a hand injury. He devoted his energies to composition and also worked as a music journalist for *The New Music Journal*, which he founded. From 1854 Schumann spent the remainder of his life in an insane asylum. His compositions include symphonies, many piano works, a piano concerto, chamber music, songs, and choral works.

Knight Ruppert*

from "Album for the Young"

STYLE: ROMANTIC

ROBERT SCHUMANN

*Knight Ruppert is a translation from the German, *Knecht Ruprecht*, a legendary figure who customarily appears at Christmas time to take children to task for misbehavior — a sort of "anti-Santa."

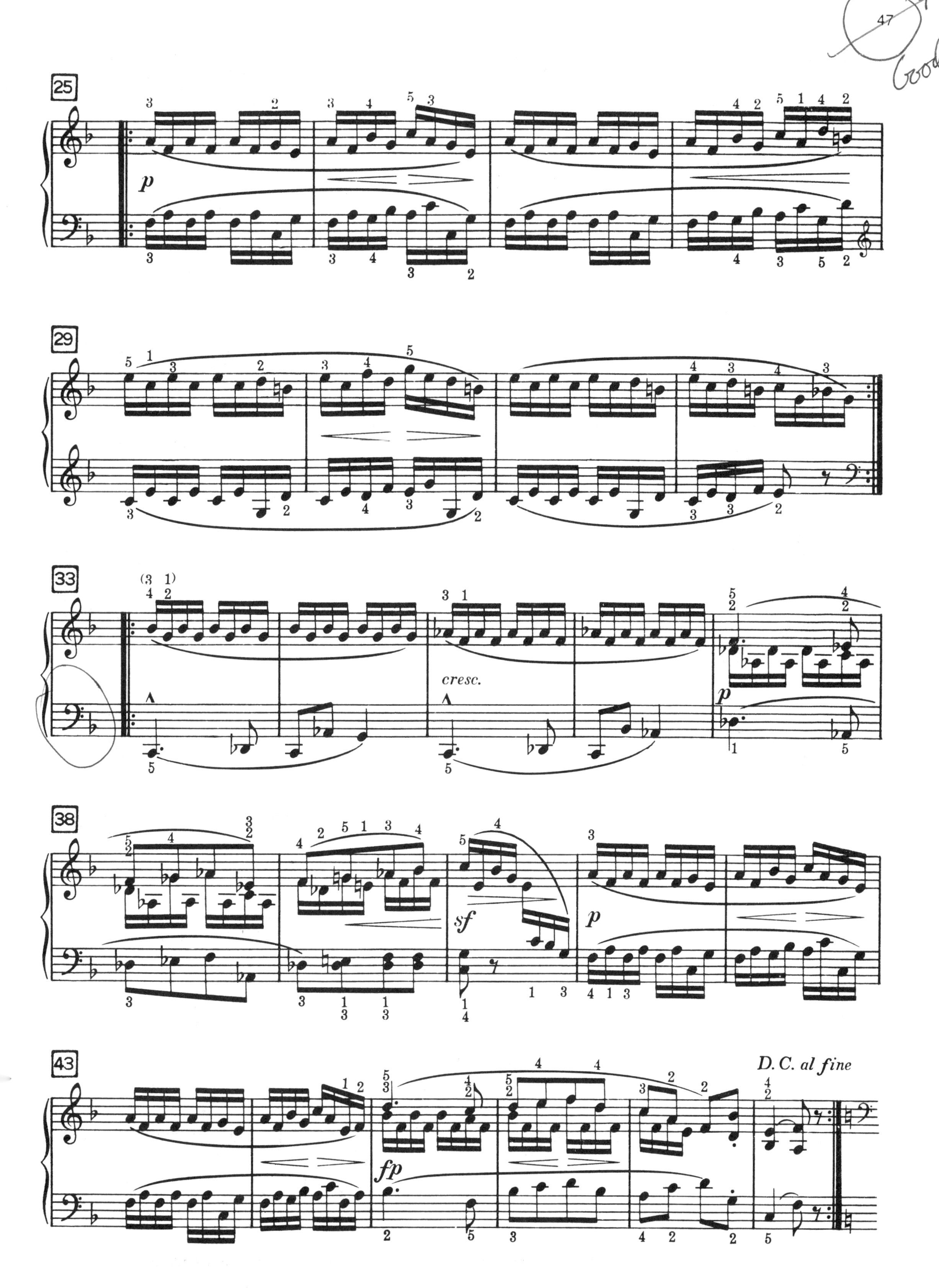

25
29
33
cresc.
38
43
D. C. al fine

THE CONTEMPORARY

New York City skyline

"The Persistence of Memory"
by Salvador Dali (1931). Oil on canvas, 9½" x 13". From The Museum of Modern Art, New York. Given Anonymously.

Contemporary Style

The Contemporary period, beginning about 1900, reflects our modern, mechanized, atomic age. Contemporary music is often angular and dissonant, portraying anxiety and the "clash and clang" of modern city life. Compared to the Romantic period, modern dress is practical, simple, and tailored. New synthetic man-made materials are frequently used in place of natural materials such as wool or cotton. Likewise, experiments with "synthetic" electronic music have produced totally new mediums for musical expression. The art and architecture of our period contain elements ranging from angular shapes to sleek, functional lines.

Contemporary Keyboard Music

The keyboard music in the Contemporary period frequently contains new sounds such as the whole-tone scale (example: D, E, F♯, G♯, A♯, C) and twelve-tone music (twelve different tones arranged in a particular sequence). Also, the music may include changing meters and an irregular number of measures (3, 5, or 7) in phrases.

from Spiders by Bastien

The accompaniment in the Contemporary period may include some dissonant chords, used for color, that do not belong to the notes in the melody.

from Follow the Leader by Bartók

PERIOD 1900-PRESENT

Contemporary Forms

Although standard forms from other eras are used, today's composers use them in personal ways to reflect their own styles. Debussy used the prelude, étude, and suite; Bartók used the forms of the bagatelle, sonata, suite, rondo, folk songs and dances; and Kabalevsky used the prelude, variations, sonata, rondo, and prelude and fugue. Brilliant display pieces such as the toccata and étude are common forms among contemporary composers as well.

The Piano in the Contemporary Period

The Contemporary piano is even larger and more resonant than the piano in the Romantic period. The modern grand has a brilliant tone necessary for projection in today's large concert halls.

Grand Piano
Grand pianos are available in several lengths ranging roughly from four to nine feet. In general, the larger the piano the better the sound.

Electronic Piano
Electronic pianos range from portable keyboards of a few octaves to instruments that look like a spinet, but have headsets for the player's use. The models shown are especially for class piano instruction.

Contemporary Composers

Within the "modern" era great style variations are found, ranging from composers such as Sergei Rachmaninoff (1873-1943) and others writing in a somewhat romantic style, to composer Claude Debussy (1862-1918) and Maurice Ravel (1975-1937) who wrote in a mildly contemporary style. George Gershwin (1898-1937) and others wrote music combining elements of jazz in a contemporary, individual style. Composers who developed new concepts of melody-tonality-rhythm include Béla Bartók (1881-1945), Igor Stravinsky (1882-1971), Serge Prokofiev (1890-1953), Aaron Copland (1900-1990), Dmitri Kabalevsky (1904-1987), Dmitri Shostakovich (1906-1975), and Samuel Barber (1910-1981).

Dmitri Kabalevsky (1904-1987), a Russian composer wrote many teaching pieces for children. Among the best-known works for students are his piano pieces, *Children's Pieces, Op. 27*; *24 Pieces for Children, Op. 39*; *Variations, Op. 40*; and the *Youth Concerto for Piano, No. 3*. In addition to composing and teaching, Kabalevsky was a conductor, music critic, musicologist, and toured as a pianist.

Toccatina

from "30 Children's Pieces," Op. 27

STYLE: CONTEMPORARY

DMITRI KABALEVSKY

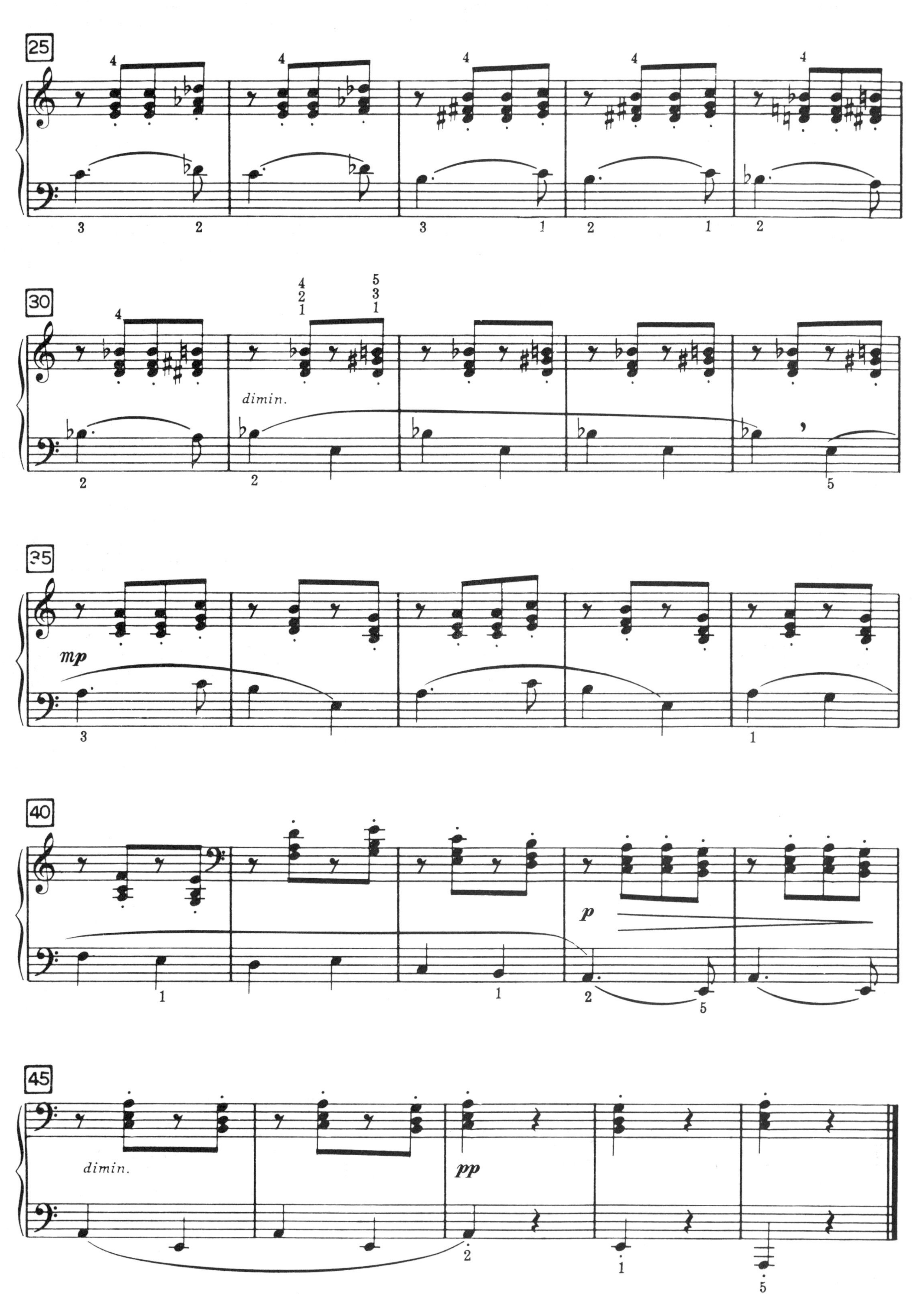
25
30
dimin.
35
mp
40
p
45
dimin.
pp

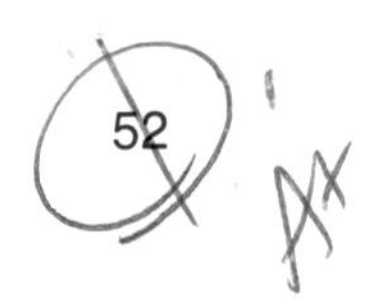

Sonatina

from "19 Children's Pieces," Op. 27

STYLE: CONTEMPORARY

DMITRI KABALEVSKY

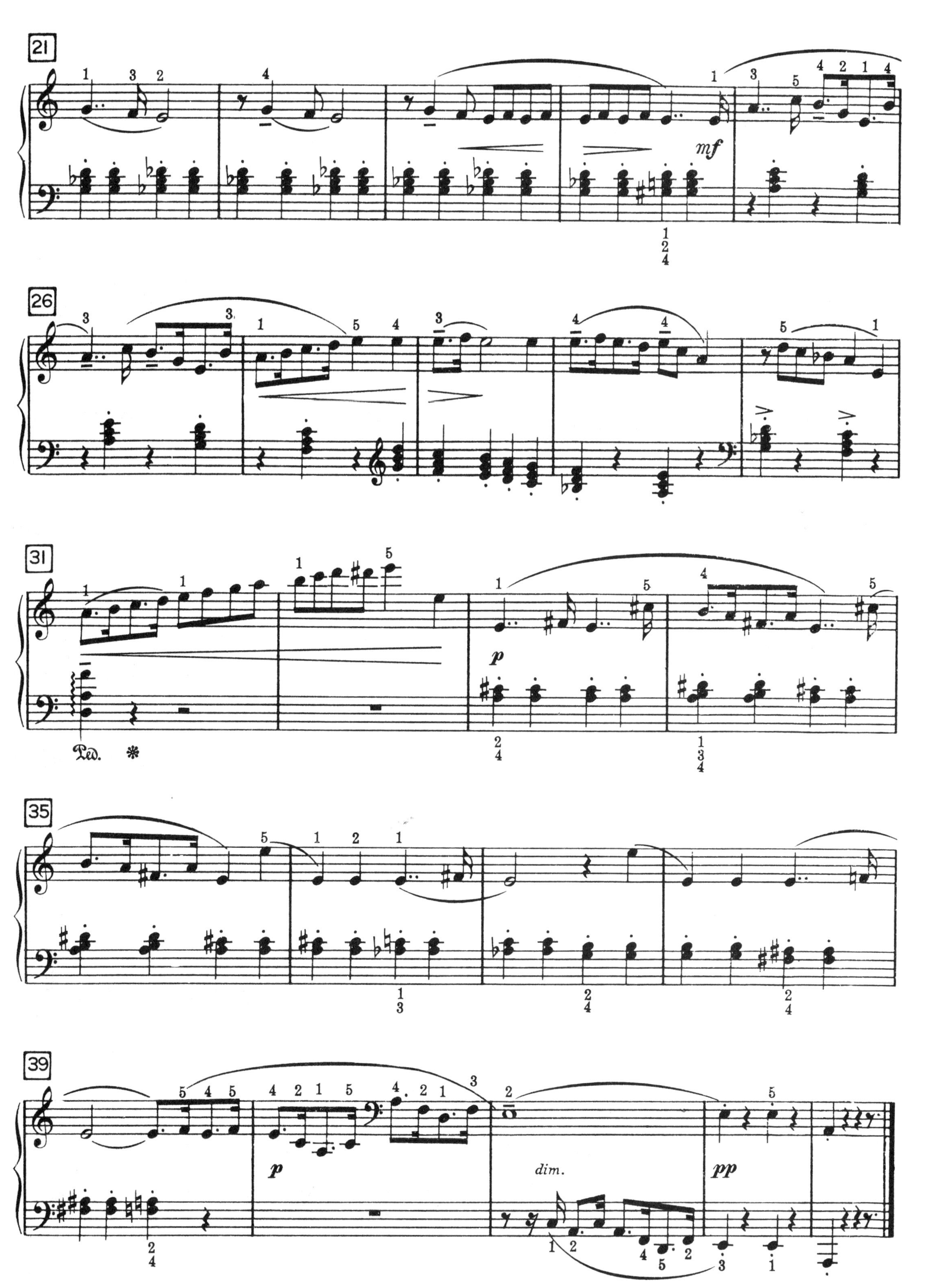
21
mf
26
31
Ped.
p
35
39
p
dim.
pp

Aram Khachaturian (1903-1978), a Russian composer, played the tuba in his school band. Later he went to Moscow and entered the Gnessin School to study cello and composition. His compositions have a broad popular appeal and include such well-known works as the *Sabre Dance* (from the ballet *Gayane*), *Piano Concerto, Violin Concerto* and piano pieces such as the *Toccata* and the suite for children, *Adventures of Ivan.*

Ivan Sings

from "Adventures of Ivan"

STYLE: CONTEMPORARY

ARAM KHACHATURIAN

16
rit.
a tempo
mf
Ped.
19
Ped. simile
22
24
f
Ped.
27
rit.
p
Ped.

The flamenco is a type of Spanish song usually performed with guitar accompaniment. Solo guitarists often play "flamenco style" which is a rather free form depicting many moods, tempos, and dynamics.

Flamenco

STYLE: CONTEMPORARY

JAMES BASTIEN

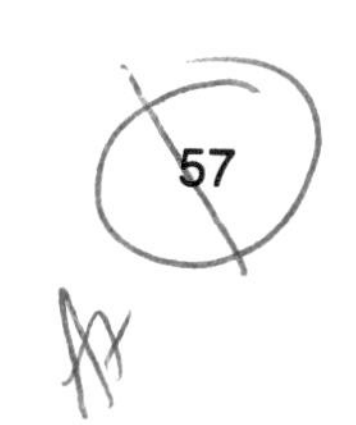
57

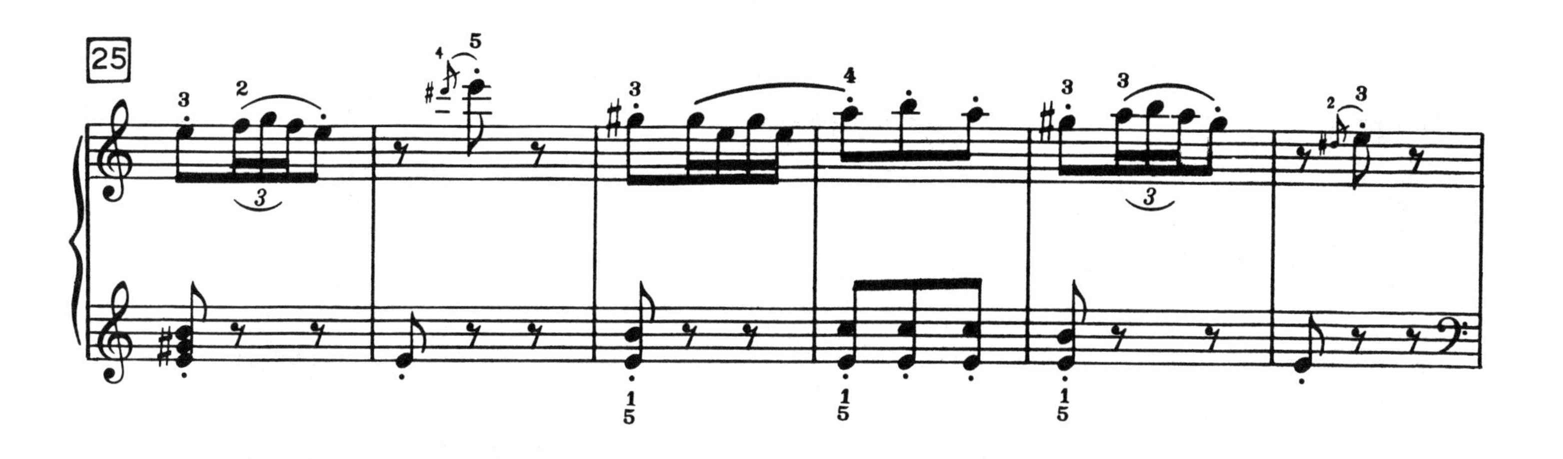
25

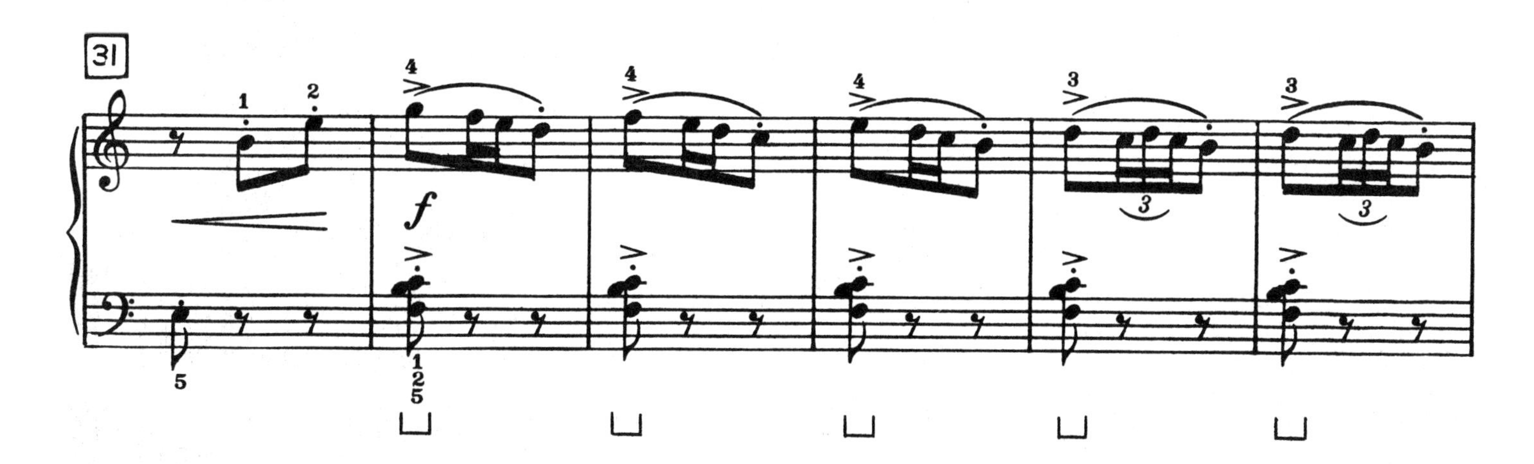
31
f

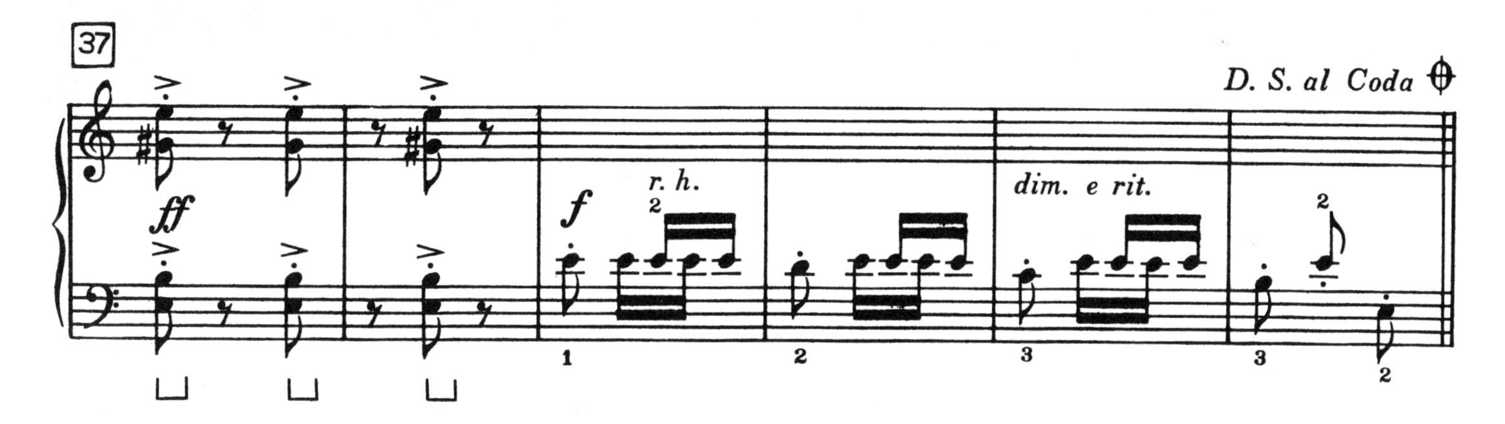
37
D. S. al Coda
ff
f
r. h.
dim. e rit.

Coda
f
r. h.
poco rit.

Variations on a Theme by Paganini

from Caprices, Op. 1, No. 25 for violin

STYLE: CONTEMPORARY

JAMES BASTIEN

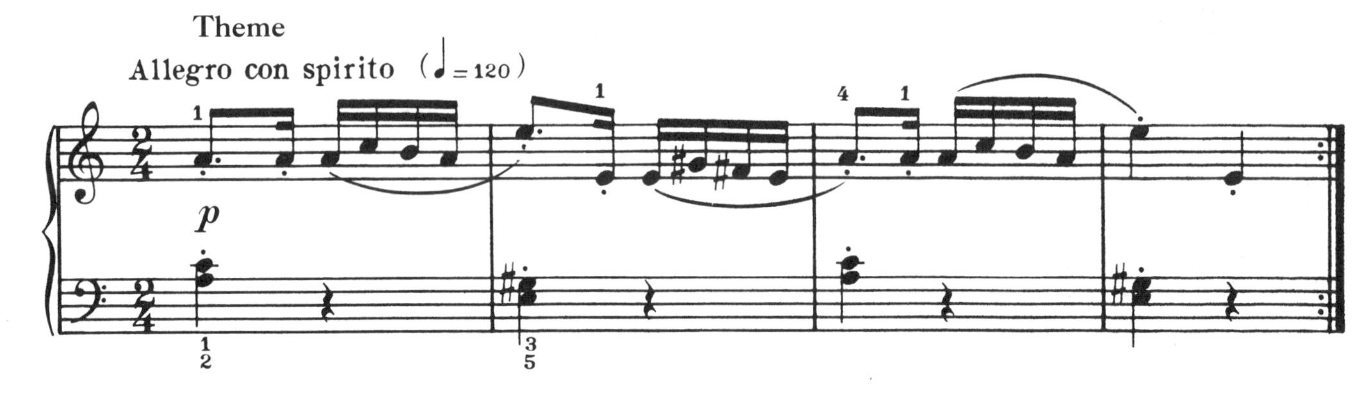

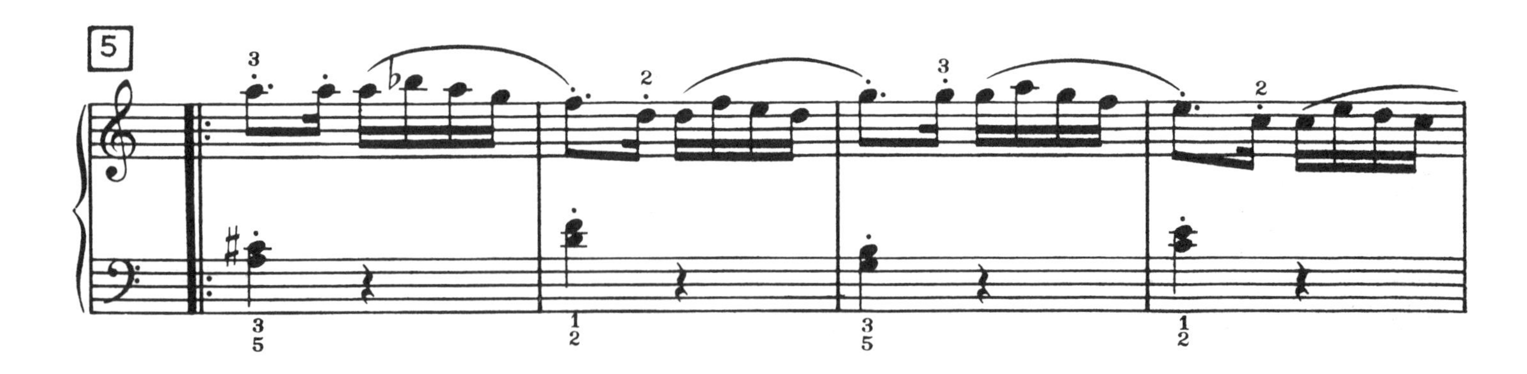

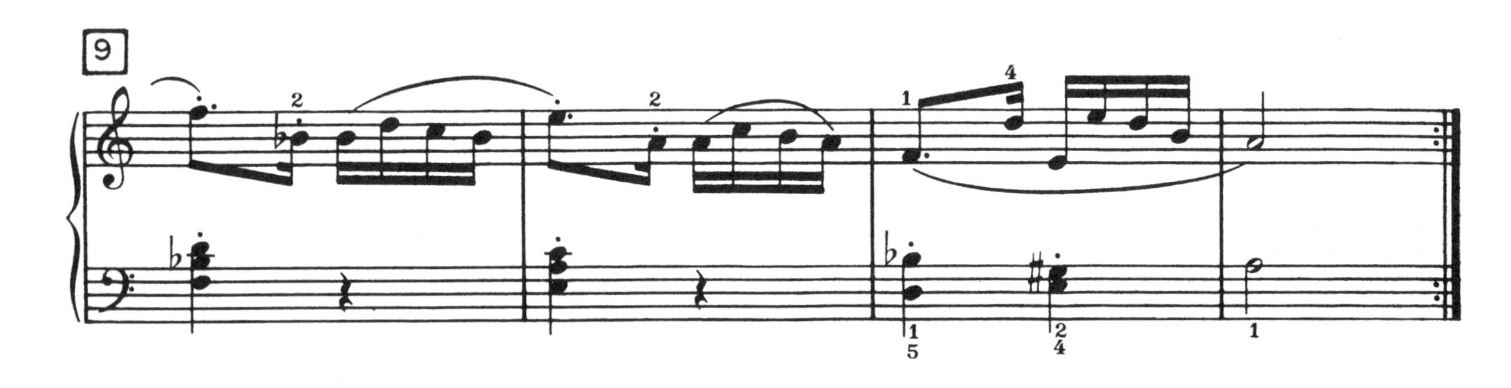

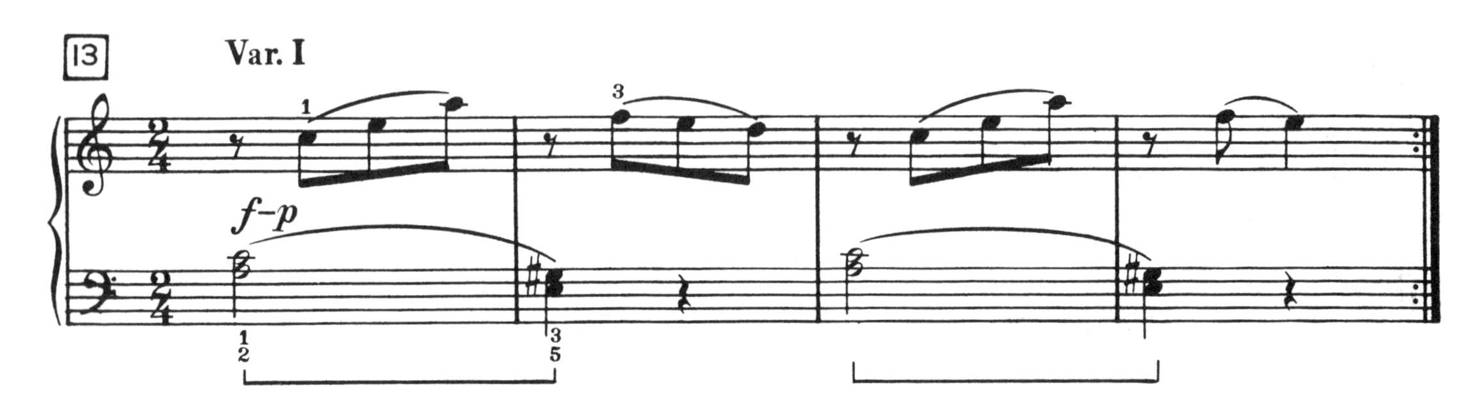

17
f
21
dim.
25
Var. II
p
29
f
33
dim.
p

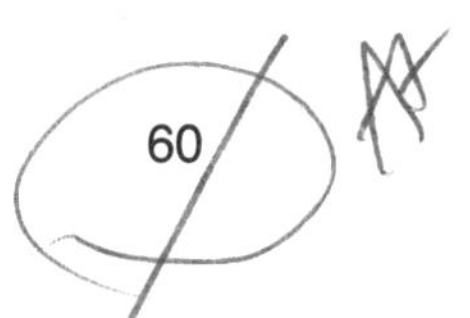

Var. III
37
sempre forte
40
43
46
Var. IV
Maestoso
50

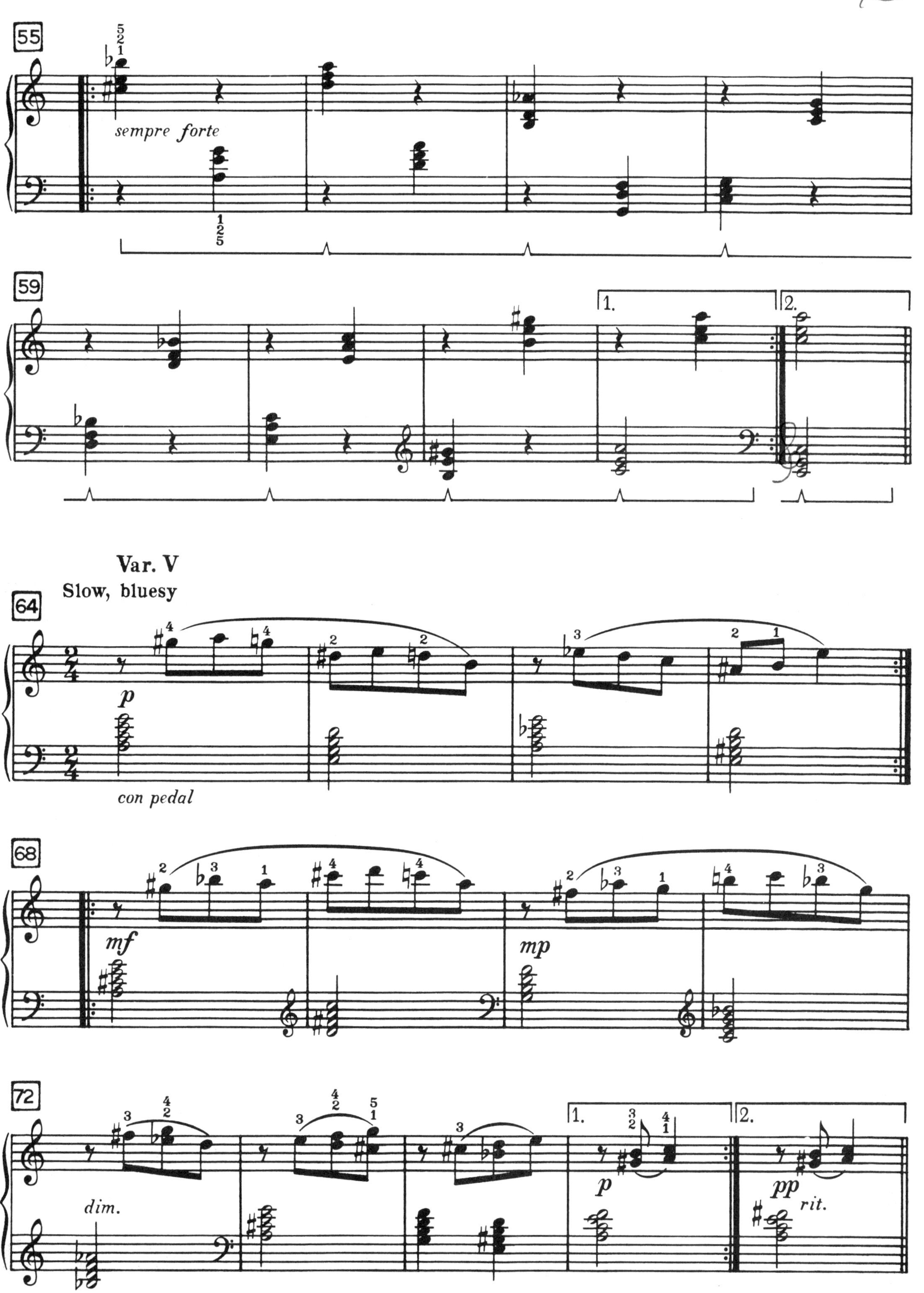

55
sempre forte
59
1.
2.
Var. V
Slow, bluesy
64
p
con pedal
68
mf
mp
72
dim.
p
pp
rit.

Var. VI
Finale
Allegro furioso
77
81
85
89
93

97
sempre forte
101
cresc.
105
ff
mf
poco
a
poco
109
accelerando
e
crescendo
113
a tempo
ff
f

Music Dictionary

TERM	ABBREVIATION or Sign	MEANING
Accelerando	*accel.*	gradually increase speed
Accent sign	>	stress and play louder
Alla Breve	𝄵	$\frac{2}{2}$ time; two strong beats to the measure
Alla marcia		in march time
Allegretto		moderately fast
Allegro		fast ("cheerful")
Andante		walking speed
Animato		lively, animated
A Tempo		return to the original speed
Cantabile		in a singing style
Coda		an added ending
Con		with
Con brio		with spirit
Con spirito		with spirit
Crescendo	*cresc.*	play gradually louder
Da Capo al Fine	*D. C. al Fine*	return to the beginning and play to the word "*Fine*"
Decrescendo	*decresc.*	play gradually softer
Del Segno al Fine	*D. S. al Fine*	return to the sign (𝄋) and play to the word "*Fine*"
Diminuendo	*dim.*	play gradually softer
Dolce		sweetly
Espressivo		with expression
Fermata	𝄐	hold the note (or notes) longer
Fine		the end
Forte	***f***	loud
Fortissimo	***ff***	very loud
Grazioso		gracefully
Largo		very slowly
Legato		smooth, connected tones
Lento		very slowly
Mezzo Forte	***mf***	moderately loud
Mezzo Piano	***mp***	moderately soft
Moderato		a moderate speed
Molto		much, very
Non		not
Octave sign	*8va*	play eight scale degrees higher (one octave) when the sign is above the notes; play eight scale degrees lower when the sign is below the notes
	15ma	play two octaves higher than written
Pianissimo	***pp***	very soft
Piano	***p***	soft
Piu		more
Poco a poco		little by little
Presto		very fast
Repeat sign	𝄇	go back and play again
Ritardando	*rit.*	play gradually slower
Scherzando		playfully
Sforzando	***sfz***	a sudden strong accent
Simile		similar
Staccato		short, disconnected tones
Subito		suddenly
Tempo		rate of speed
Tenuto sign	–	held, sustained for full value
Tie		connects two notes on the same line or space; hold the notes for their combined value.
Vivace		lively, quick
Vivo		lively